ATI TEAS 6

Math workbook

Activities, Exercises, and Two Complete ATI TEAS Mathematics Practice Tests

By

Michael Smith & Reza Nazari

ATI TEAS 6 Math Workbook

Published in the United State of America By

The Math Notion

Email: info@Mathnotion.com

Web: www.MathNotion.com

About the Author

Michael Smith has been a math instructor for over a decade now. He holds a master's degree in Management. Since 2006, Michael has devoted his time to both teaching and developing exceptional math learning materials. As a Math instructor and test prep expert, Michael has worked with thousands of students. He has used the feedback of his students to develop a unique study program that can be used by students to drastically improve their math score fast and effectively.

– DAT Math Workbook

– TASC Math Workbook

– HiSET Math Workbook

– AFOQT Math Workbook

–many Math Education Workbooks

– and some Mathematics books …

As an experienced Math teacher, Mr. Smith employs a variety of formats to help students achieve their goals: He tutors online and in person, he teaches students in large groups, and he provides training materials and textbooks through his website and through Amazon.

You can contact Michael via email at:

info@Mathnotion.com

ATI TEAS Math Workbook

ATI TEAS Math Workbook reviews all ATI TEAS Math topics and provides students with the confidence and math skills they need to succeed on the ATI TEAS Math. It is designed to address the needs of ATI TEAS test takers who must have a working knowledge of basic Mathematics.

This comprehensive workbook with over 2,500 sample questions and 2 complete ATI TEAS tests can help you fully prepare for the ATI TEAS Math test. It provides you with an in-depth focus on the math portion of the exam, helping you master the math skills that students find the most troublesome. This is an incredibly useful tool for those who want to review all topics being covered on the ATI TEAS Math test.

ATI TEAS Math Workbook contains many exciting features to help you prepare for the ATI TEAS Math test, including:

- Content 100% aligned with the 2019-2020 ATI TEAS test
- Provided and tested by ATI TEAS Math test experts
- Dynamic design and easy-to-follow activities
- A fun, interactive and concrete learning process
- Targeted, skill-building practices
- Complete coverage of all ATI TEAS Math topics which you will be tested
- 2 full-length practice tests (featuring new question types) with detailed answers.

The only prep book you will ever need to ace the ATI TEAS Math Test!

WWW.MathNotion.COM

… So Much More Online!

✓ FREE Math Lessons

✓ More Math Learning Books!

✓ Mathematics Worksheets

✓ Online Math Tutors

For a PDF Version of This Book

Please Visit WWW.MathNotion.com

Contents

Chapter 1: Whole Numbers, Real Numbers and Integers **11**

Rounding and Estimates 12

Whole Number Addition and Subtraction 13

Whole Number Multiplication and Division 14

Adding and Subtracting Integers 15

Multiplying and Dividing Integers 16

Arrange, Order, and Comparing Integers 17

Order of Operations 18

Integers and Absolute Value 19

Answers of Worksheets – Chapter 1 20

Chapter 2: Fractions and Decimals **23**

Simplifying Fractions 24

Factoring Numbers 25

Greatest Common Factor (GCF) 26

Least Common Multiple (LCM) 26

Divisibility Rules 27

Adding and Subtracting Fractions 28

Multiplying and Dividing Fractions 29

Adding and Subtracting Mixed Numbers 30

Multiplying and Dividing Mixed Numbers 31

Comparing Decimals 32

Rounding Decimals 33

Adding and Subtracting Decimals 34

Multiplying and Dividing Decimals 35

Converting Between Fractions, Decimals and Mixed Numbers 36

Answers of Worksheets – Chapter 2 37

Chapter 3: Proportion, Ratio, Percent **43**

Writing and Simplifying Ratios 44

Create a Proportion 45

Similar Figures 45

Ratio and Rates Word Problems...46

Percentage Calculations..47

Percent Problems 48

Markup, Discount, and Tax 48

Simple Interest 49

Converting Between Percent, Fractions, and Decimals......................................50

Answers of Worksheets – Chapter 3 51

Chapter 4: Exponents and Radicals 53

Multiplication Property of Exponents...54

Division Property of Exponents 54

Powers of Products and Quotients 55

Zero and Negative Exponents 56

Negative Exponents and Negative Bases 56

Writing Scientific Notation 57

Square Roots 57

Answers of Worksheets – Chapter 4 58

Chapter 5: Algebraic Expressions 61

Translate Phrases into an Algebraic Statement..62

The Distributive Property...62

Evaluating One Variable 63

Evaluating Two Variables 63

Expressions and Variables..64

Combining like Terms..65

Simplifying Polynomial Expressions...66

Answers of Worksheets – Chapter 5...67

Chapter 6: Equations and Inequalities.. 69

One–Step Equations 70

Two–Step Equations 71

Multi–Step Equations 72

Graphing Single–Variable Inequalities 73

One–Step Inequalities...74

Two–Step Inequalities...75

Multi–Step Inequalities 75

Solving Systems of Equations by Substitution 76

Solving Systems of Equations by Elimination 77

Systems of Equations Word Problems 78

Linear Equations 79

Graphing Lines of Equations 80

Graphing Linear Inequalities 81

Finding Distance of Two Points 82

Answers of Worksheets – Chapter 6 83

Chapter 7: Polynomials **89**

Classifying Polynomials 90

Simplifying Polynomials 91

Adding and Subtracting Polynomials 92

Multiplying Monomials 92

Multiply and Divide Monomials 93

Multiply a Polynomial and a Monomial 93

Multiply Binomials 94

Factor Trinomials 94

Operations with Polynomials 95

Answers of Worksheets – Chapter 7 96

Chapter 8: Geometry **99**

The Pythagorean Theorem 100

Angles 101

Area of Triangles... 102

Area of Trapezoids 103

Area and Perimeter of Polygons... 104

Area and Circumference of Circles... 106

Volume of Cubes 107

Volume of Rectangle Prisms.. 108

Surface Area of Cubes 109

Surface Area of a Rectangle Prism 110

Volume of a Cylinder 111

Surface Area of a Cylinder 112

Answers of Worksheets – Chapter 8...113

Chapter 9: Statistics 115

Mean and Median..116

Mode and Range..117

Times Series 118

Box and Whisker Plot 119

Bar Graph 119

Dot plots..120

Scatter Plots 121

Stem–And–Leaf Plot 122

The Pie Graph or Circle Graph...123

Probability of Simple Events 124

Answers of Worksheets – Chapter 9 125

ATI TEAS 6 Test Review... 129

ATI TEAS 6 Mathematics Practice Tests Answer Sheets.......................................131

ATI TEAS 6 Practice Test 1 133

ATI TEAS 6 Practice Test 2 147

Answers and Explanations.. 161

Answer Key...161

Practice Test 1 163

Practice Test 2 169

Chapter 1: Whole Numbers, Real Numbers and Integers

Topics that you'll learn in this chapter:

- ➤ Rounding and Estimates

- ➤ Addition, Subtraction, Multiplication and Division Whole Number and Integers

- ➤ Arrange and ordering Integers and Numbers

- ➤ Comparing Integers, Order of Operations

- ➤ Mixed Integer Computations

- ➤ Integers and Absolute Value

"If people do not believe that mathematics is simple, it is only because they do not realize how complicated life is." — John von Neumann

Rounding and Estimates

Round each number to the underlined place value.

1) <u>8</u>8

2) <u>8</u>.15

3) <u>4</u>,315

4) 5<u>6</u>5

5) 1.<u>3</u>31

6) 1<u>8</u>.175

7) <u>2</u>.429

8) <u>3</u>85

9) 14.<u>2</u>3

10) 2,<u>9</u>97

11) 4.3<u>1</u>3

12) <u>7</u>.38

Estimate the sum by rounding each added to the nearest ten.

1) 17 + 18

2) 11 + 55

3) 203 + 56

4) 57 + 38

5) 213 + 74

6) 94 + 81

7) 19 + 167

8) 55 + 33

9) 96 + 49

10) 99 + 324

11) 823 + 488

12) 466 + 276

13) 5112 + 5792

14) 1245 + 2459

15) 5265 + 382

Whole Number Addition and Subtraction

🖊 **Solve.**

1) Erika has just started her first job after graduating from college. Her yearly income is $30,000 per year. Erika's father income is $47,000 per year and her mother's income is $40,000. What is yearly income of Erika and her parents altogether?

2) A school had 708 students last year. If all last year students and 218 new students have registered for this year, how many students will there be in total?

3) Daniel has 820 marbles, Ethan has 500 marbles, and Emily has 340 marbles less than Daniel. How many marbles do they have in all?

4) Lisa had $856 dollars in her saving account. She gave $295 dollars to her brother, Tom. How much money does she have left?

🖊 **Find the missing number.**

5) 540– .... = 100

6) 800 – .... = 220

7) .... − 2650 = 6700

8) 85000 − 42000 = ...

13

Whole Number Multiplication and Division

✎ **Multiply and divide.**

1) $120 \times 6 =$

2) $160 \times 30 =$

3) $600 \times 30 =$

4) $420 \times 20 =$

5) $250 \times 40 =$

6) $600 \times 40 =$

7) $215 \times 70 =$

8) $2000 \div 80 =$

9) $225 \div 25 =$

10) $315 \div 15 =$

11) $384 \div 12 =$

12) $740 \div 4 =$

13) $1925 \div 7 =$

14) $494 \div 13 =$

15) Alice and her two brothers have 7 boxes of crayons. Each box contains 66 crayons. How many crayons do Alice and her two brothers have?

16) A group of 125 students has collected $7236 for charity during last month. They decided to split the money evenly among 6 charities. How much will each charity receive?

Adding and Subtracting Integers

✎ **Find the sum.**

1) $(-12) + (-3)$

2) $8 + (-11)$

3) $(-13) + 25$

4) $(-7) + 37$

5) $55 + (-15)$

6) $(-13) + (-4) + 5$

7) $2 + (-11) + (-30) + (9)$

8) $(-25) + (-11) + 36 + 9$

9) $(-5) + (-10) + (7 - 19)$

10) $3 + (-15) + (28 - 10)$

11) $(+35) + (+15) + (-20)$

12) $24 + 16 + (-13)$

✎ **Find the difference.**

13) $(-3) - (-2\ 3)$

14) $(-12) - (33)$

15) $(38) - (-12)$

16) $(55) - (21)$

17) $(-11) - (-5) - (10)$

18) $(50) - (-5) + (-25)$

19) $(4) - (-5) - (-3)$

20) $(12) - (3) - (-8)$

21) $(32) - (2) - (-20)$

22) $(-20) - (-44)$

23) $(-9) - 13 + 20$

24) $12 - (15) - (-13)$

Multiplying and Dividing Integers

🖎 **Find each product.**

1) $(-8) \times (-5)$

2) 12×3

3) $(-2) \times 5 \times (-4)$

4) $4 \times (-5) \times (-6)$

5) $11 \times (-10)$

6) $32 \times (-4)$

7) 21×3

8) $(-12) \times (-4)$

9) $3 \times (-5) \times 7$

10) $6 \times (-4) \times 3$

11) $(-11) \times (-5)$

12) $(-4) \times (-3) \times 5$

🖎 **Find each quotient.**

13) $72 \div 9$

14) $(-84) \div 7$

15) $(-95) \div (-5)$

16) $72 \div (+9)$

17) $39 \div 3$

18) $(-99) \div (-11)$

19) $22 \div (-11)$

20) $(-123) \div 1$

21) $60 \div 4$

22) $(-26) \div (-2)$

23) $(-44) \div (-11)$

24) $(-0) \div 15$

Arrange, Order, and Comparing Integers

✍ Order each set of integers from least to greatest.

1) 2, 6, − 15, − 11, 1   ___, ___, ___, ___, ___, ___

2) 9, − 8, 3, − 2 ,11   ___, ___, ___, ___, ___, ___

3) 36, − 12, 5, 1, − 2   ___, ___, ___, ___, ___, ___

4) 31, 18, 0, − 54, 9, − 5   ___, ___, ___, ___, ___, ___

5) − 15, −25, −37, 7, 0, 9   ___, ___, ___, ___, ___, ___

6) − 55, − 23, −11, 0, 3, 7   ___, ___, ___, ___, ___, ___

✍ Order each set of integers from greatest to least.

7) 1,17, 6, 8, 65, 2   ___, ___, ___, ___, ___, ___

8) − 12,6, −7, 2, − 11   ___, ___, ___, ___, ___, ___

9) − 14, 17, 7, 37, 9   ___, ___, ___, ___, ___, ___

10) − 54, 0, 14,19, 15   ___, ___, ___, ___, ___, ___

11) 12, 7, −1, − 11, 9, -3   ___, ___, ___, ___, ___, ___

12) − 14, − 7, 98, 29, 28, 3   ___, ___, ___, ___, ___, ___

✍ Compare. Use >, =, <

1) 4 _____ 3

2) − 22 _____ −11

3) 0 _____ − 31

4) −41 _____ −12

5) − 64 _____ −64

6) −1 42 _____ −1 48

7) 68 _____ 100

8) − 106 _____ − 106

9) 16 _____ − (− 16)

10) 405 _____ − 405

Order of Operations

✍ Evaluate each expression.

1) $24 - (8 \times 6)$

2) $5 \times 6 - (\frac{15}{11 - (-4)})$

3) $12 - (6 \times (-3))$

4) $(6 \times 7) + (-7)$

5) $(\frac{(-1) + 4}{(-1) + (-2)}) \times (-9)$

6) $(16 + (-4) - 2) \times 7 - 25$

7) $\frac{30}{2(9 - (-1)) - 10}$

8) $58 - (6 \times 9)$

9) $13 + (4 \times 2)$

10) $((-3) + 15) \div (-3)$

11) $[(-8 \div 2) \div (2 - 4))$

12) $34 + (-5) \times (\frac{(-12)}{10})$

Integers and Absolute Value

✏️ Write absolute value of each number.

1) 62

2) − 32

3) − 11

4) 5

5) 17

6) − 12

7) − 9

8) 0

9) -14

10) − 7

11) −33

12) 25

13) − 34

14) − 55

✏️ Evaluate.

15) $|-12| - |3| + 2$

16) $19 + |-5 - 14| - |2|$

17) $38 - |-17| - 3$

18) $|26| - |-12| + 9$

19) $|91| - |-18| - 18$

20) $|13| - |-18| + 40$

21) $|-77 + 17| + 15 - 5$

22) $|-11| + |-9|$

23) $|-12 + 4 - 2| + |3 + 6|$

24) $|-40| - |-20| - 3$

25) $|-10 + 4| \times \frac{|-7 \times 5|}{7}$

26) $\frac{|-16 \times 3|}{2} \times |-12| =$

Answers of Worksheets – Chapter 1

Rounding

1) 90	5) 1.3	9) 14.2
2) 8.000	6) 18.00	10) 3,000
3) 4,000	7) 2.000	11) 4.300
4) 570	8) 400	12) 7.000

Rounding and Estimates

1) 40	6) 170	11) 1,310
2) 70	7) 190	12) 750
3) 260	8) 90	13) 10,900
4) 100	9) 150	14) 3,710
5) 280	10) 420	15) 5,650

Whole Number Addition and Subtraction

1) 117,000	4) 561	7) 9,350
2) 926	5) 440	8) 43,000
3) 1,800	6) 580	

Whole Number Multiplication and Division

1) 720	7) 15,050	13) 275
2) 4,800	8) 25	14) 38
3) 18,000	9) 9	15) 462
4) 8,400	10) 21	16) 1,206
5) 10,000	11) 32	
6) 24,000	12) 185	

Adding and Subtracting Integers

1) − 15	5) 40	9) − 27
2) − 3	6) − 12	10) 6
3) 12	7) − 30	11) 30
4) 30	8) 9	12) 27

13) 20

14) −45

15) 50

16) 34

17) −16

18) 30

19) 12

20) 17

21) 50

22) 24

23) −2

24) 10

Multiplying and Dividing Integers

1) 40

2) 36

3) 40

4) 120

5) − 110

6) − 128

7) 63

8) 48

9) 105

10) −72

11) 55

12) 60

13) 8

14) − 12

15) 19

16) 8

17) 13

18) 9

19) −2

20) −123

21) 15

22) 13

23) 4

24) 0

Arrange and Order, Comparing Integers

1) − 15, − 11, 1, 2, 6

2) − 8, − 2, 3, 9 ,11

3) − 12, − 2, 1, 5, 36

4) −54, −5, 0, 9, 18, 31

5) − 37, − 25, −15, 0, 7, 9

6) −55, −23, −11, 0, 3 ,7

7) 65, 17, 8, 6, 2, 1

8) 6, 2, − 7, − 11, − 12

9) 37, 17, 9, 7, −14

10) 19, 15, 14, 0, −54

11) 12, 9, 7, −1, −3, −11

12) 98, 29, 28, 3, −7, −14

Compare.

1) >

2) <

3) >

4) <

5) =

6) >

7) <

8) =

9) =

10) >

Order of Operations

1) −24

2) 29

3) 30

4) 35

5) 9

6) 45

7) 3

8) 4

9) 21

10) −4

11) 2

12) 40

Integers and Absolute Value

1) 62

2) 32

3) 11

4) 5

5) 17

6) 12

7) 9

8) 0

9) 14

10) 7

11) 33

12) 25

13) 34

14) 55

15) 11

16) 36

17) 18

18) 23

19) 55

20) 35

21) 70

22) 20

23) 19

24) 17

25) 30

26) 288

Chapter 2: Fractions and Decimals

Topics that you'll learn in this chapter:

> Simplifying Fractions

> Adding and Subtracting Fractions, Mixed Numbers and Decimals

> Multiplying and Dividing Fractions, Mixed Numbers and Decimals

> Comparing and Rounding Decimals

> Converting Between Fractions, Decimals and Mixed Numbers

> Factoring Numbers, Greatest Common Factor, and Least Common Multiple

> Divisibility Rules

"A Man is like a fraction whose numerator is what he is and whose denominator is what he thinks of himself. The larger the denominator, the smaller the fraction." –Tolstoy

Simplifying Fractions

✍ **Simplify the fractions.**

1) $\dfrac{44}{64}$

2) $\dfrac{12}{26}$

3) $\dfrac{15}{25}$

4) $\dfrac{30}{45}$

5) $\dfrac{18}{27}$

6) $\dfrac{30}{90}$

7) $\dfrac{14}{36}$

8) $\dfrac{24}{58}$

9) $\dfrac{30}{90}$

10) $\dfrac{6}{54}$

11) $\dfrac{35}{55}$

12) $\dfrac{28}{38}$

13) $5\dfrac{40}{64}$

14) $2\dfrac{24}{42}$

15) $9\dfrac{5}{35}$

16) $3\dfrac{45}{75}$

17) $1\dfrac{62}{124}$

18) $4\dfrac{12}{66}$

19) $1\dfrac{55}{70}$

20) $\dfrac{54}{60}$

21) $7\dfrac{68}{136}$

Factoring Numbers

✍ List all positive factors of each number.

1) 90

2) 12

3) 49

4) 100

5) 50

6) 64

7) 34

8) 27

9) 63

10) 110

11) 96

12) 48

✍ List the prime factorization for each number.

13) 40

14) 210

15) 105

16) 24

17) 42

18) 66

19) 78

20) 165

21) 125

22) 32

23) 12

24) 23

25) 60

26) 54

Greatest Common Factor (GCF)

✎ **Find the GCF for each number pair.**

1) 12, 25	7) 18, 24	13) 72, 84
2) 24, 36	8) 80, 130	14) 30, 45
3) 9, 36	9) 60, 80	15) 63, 42
4) 27, 12	10) 21, 14	16) 125, 50
5) 54, 39	11) 64, 32	17) 36, 52
6) 66, 77	12) 90, 45	18) 165, 60

Least Common Multiple (LCM)

✎ **Find the LCM for each number pair.**

1) 12, 18	7) 84, 60	13) 12, 18, 24
2) 15, 30	8) 42, 18	14) 10, 15, 35
3) 60, 40	9) 52, 78	15) 14, 27, 54
4) 14, 28	10) 15, 12	16) 3, 11, 13
5) 24, 32	11) 72, 6	17) 14, 7, 42
6) 40, 20	12) 10, 30, 60	18) 72, 66, 24

Divisibility Rules

🖎 **Use the divisibility rules to find the factors of each number.**

1) 12   2 3 4 5 6 7 8 9

2) 24   2 3 4 5 6 7 8 9

3) 36   2 3 4 5 6 7 8 9

4) 18   2 3 4 5 6 7 8 9

5) 30   2 3 4 5 6 7 8 9

6) 54   2 3 4 5 6 7 8 9

7) 64   2 3 4 5 6 7 8 9

8) 42   2 3 4 5 6 7 8 9

9) 90   2 3 4 5 6 7 8 9

10) 80   2 3 4 5 6 7 8 9

11) 72   2 3 4 5 6 7 8 9

12) 84   2 3 4 5 6 7 8 9

Adding and Subtracting Fractions

✏️ **Add fractions.**

1) $\dfrac{1}{4} + \dfrac{2}{3}$ 4) $\dfrac{2}{15} + \dfrac{4}{15}$ 7) $\dfrac{3}{4} + \dfrac{1}{2}$

2) $\dfrac{1}{3} + \dfrac{1}{2}$ 5) $\dfrac{1}{12} + \dfrac{2}{3}$ 8) $\dfrac{6}{7} + \dfrac{3}{21}$

3) $\dfrac{1}{4} + \dfrac{5}{7}$ 6) $\dfrac{3}{7} + \dfrac{2}{3}$ 9) $\dfrac{5}{13} + \dfrac{1}{2}$

✏️ **Subtract fractions.**

10) $\dfrac{1}{2} - \dfrac{1}{5}$ 13) $\dfrac{2}{3} - \dfrac{2}{7}$ 16) $\dfrac{3}{4} - \dfrac{1}{3}$

11) $\dfrac{1}{7} - \dfrac{1}{9}$ 14) $\dfrac{8}{15} - \dfrac{1}{5}$ 17) $\dfrac{1}{3} - \dfrac{1}{4}$

12) $\dfrac{3}{5} - \dfrac{1}{15}$ 15) $\dfrac{3}{8} - \dfrac{2}{12}$ 18) $\dfrac{6}{5} - \dfrac{5}{6}$

Multiplying and Dividing Fractions

✍ Multiplying fractions. Then simplify.

1) $\dfrac{3}{5} \times \dfrac{5}{9}$

2) $\dfrac{6}{49} \times \dfrac{7}{3}$

3) $\dfrac{5}{21} \times \dfrac{7}{10}$

4) $\dfrac{8}{33} \times \dfrac{11}{24}$

5) $\dfrac{3}{29} \times \dfrac{29}{3}$

6) $0 \times \dfrac{103}{28}$

7) $\dfrac{8}{11} \times 11$

8) $\dfrac{2}{5} \times \dfrac{10}{3}$

9) $\dfrac{7}{9} \times \dfrac{12}{28}$

10) $\dfrac{13}{5} \times \dfrac{15}{26}$

✍ Dividing fractions.

11) $3 \div \dfrac{9}{7}$

12) $\dfrac{4}{9} \div 4$

13) $0 \div \dfrac{2}{5}$

14) $\dfrac{32}{25} \div \dfrac{8}{5}$

15) $\dfrac{5}{21} \div \dfrac{2}{21}$

16) $\dfrac{2}{7} \div \dfrac{8}{35}$

17) $\dfrac{3}{5} \div \dfrac{4}{5}$

18) $\dfrac{12}{25} \div \dfrac{3}{5}$

19) $\dfrac{3}{8} \div \dfrac{2}{5}$

20) $7 \div \dfrac{2}{3}$

21) $\dfrac{6}{7} \div \dfrac{9}{28}$

22) $\dfrac{5}{32} \div \dfrac{3}{16}$

Adding and Subtracting Mixed Numbers

✏ Add.

1) $2\frac{1}{3} + 1\frac{2}{3}$

2) $3\frac{1}{2} + 1\frac{1}{4}$

3) $1\frac{1}{7} + 2\frac{1}{3}$

4) $1\frac{1}{2} + 3\frac{2}{3}$

5) $1\frac{2}{5} + 2\frac{1}{10}$

6) $7 + 2\frac{1}{2}$

7) $4\frac{1}{3} + 2\frac{2}{3}$

8) $2\frac{2}{3} + 1\frac{1}{4}$

9) $2\frac{3}{4} + 3\frac{1}{8}$

10) $9 + 1\frac{1}{9}$

11) $4\frac{5}{12} + 2\frac{3}{4}$

12) $3\frac{1}{7} + 2\frac{3}{14}$

✏ Subtract.

1) $5\frac{2}{7} - 2\frac{1}{14}$

2) $4\frac{2}{5} - \frac{2}{3}$

3) $3\frac{3}{7} - 1\frac{1}{14}$

4) $7\frac{2}{5} - 5\frac{1}{3}$

5) $4\frac{1}{2} - 1\frac{3}{2}$

6) $5\frac{2}{3} - 2\frac{4}{3}$

7) $7\frac{5}{12} - 5\frac{7}{12}$

8) $5\frac{2}{9} - 2\frac{1}{18}$

9) $3\frac{2}{5} - 2\frac{1}{5}$

10) $3\frac{4}{9} - 1\frac{2}{9}$

11) $7\frac{4}{5} - 3\frac{1}{4}$

12) $4\frac{1}{12} - 3\frac{1}{18}$

Multiplying and Dividing Mixed Numbers

✏️ **Find each product.**

1) $2\frac{1}{3} \times \frac{1}{2}$

2) $1\frac{2}{5} \times \frac{2}{3}$

3) $2\frac{4}{3} \times 2\frac{2}{6}$

4) $2\frac{1}{2} \times 1\frac{2}{4}$

5) $3\frac{1}{2} \times 1\frac{2}{3}$

6) $1\frac{1}{7} \times 1\frac{3}{4}$

7) $1\frac{1}{4} \times 2\frac{6}{5}$

8) $3\frac{1}{2} \times 4\frac{2}{5}$

9) $1\frac{2}{5} \times 2\frac{1}{3}$

10) $2\frac{1}{3} \times 1\frac{3}{2}$

11) $3\frac{1}{3} \times 2\frac{1}{2}$

12) $2\frac{2}{3} \times 3\frac{3}{5}$

✏️ **Find each quotient.**

1) $2\frac{2}{3} \div 1\frac{3}{7}$

2) $1\frac{2}{5} \div 2\frac{1}{3}$

3) $2\frac{3}{5} \div 1\frac{3}{8}$

4) $\frac{3}{2} \div 2\frac{3}{4}$

5) $1\frac{4}{7} \div 2\frac{2}{3}$

6) $1\frac{2}{3} \div 2\frac{1}{3}$

7) $0 \div 4\frac{2}{5}$

8) $2\frac{2}{5} \div 1\frac{1}{2}$

9) $1\frac{2}{3} \div 2\frac{1}{5}$

10) $3\frac{2}{7} \div 4\frac{3}{5}$

11) $1\frac{1}{4} \div 2\frac{4}{5}$

12) $2 \div 3\frac{1}{3}$

Comparing Decimals

✎ Write the correct comparison symbol (>, < or =).

1) 0.025 ____ 0.25

2) 0.9 ____ 0.888

3) 4.510 ____ 4.150

4) 1 0.01 ____ 10.10

5) 0.987 ____ 0.991

6) 0.321 ____ 0.421

7) 5.210 ____ 5.211

8) 9.64 ____ 9.640

9) 43.012 ____ 43.030

10) 4.101 ____ 4.001

11) 5.012 ____ 5.010

12) 0.050 ____ 0.05

13) 5.120 ____ 5.212

14) 2.54 ____ 2.045

15) 1.490 ____ 1.049

16) 18.004 ____ 18.040

17) 0.020 ____ 0.20

18) 0.071____ 0.700

19) 0.08____ 0.009

20) 0.690 ____ 0.609

Rounding Decimals

✎ Round each decimal number to the nearest place indicated.

1) 1.8_2_

2) 0.9_4_

3) 12.6_6_3

4) 4._6_77

5) _2_.907

6) 0.98_9_

7) 11.1_4_

8) 13._8_

9) 7.91_9_

10) 8._6_95

11) 6.0_8_

12) 12._2_67

13) 9._3_01

14) 10.07_1_

15) 5_5_.89

16) 5_9_.15

17) 3_2_9.018

18) 92._4_10

19) 1.4_9_9

20) 2_5_.15

21) 67.7_0_9

22) 173._1_83

23) 32._2_81

24) 4._0_94

25) 0.0_3_21

26) 10.4_6_9

27) 2._2_91

Adding and Subtracting Decimals

✎ **Add and subtract decimals.**

1)
$$\begin{array}{r} 87.15 \\ -\ 32.35 \\ \hline \end{array}$$

4)
$$\begin{array}{r} 65.23 \\ -\ 56.48 \\ \hline \end{array}$$

2)
$$\begin{array}{r} 90.43 \\ +\ 44.09 \\ \hline \end{array}$$

5)
$$\begin{array}{r} 98.125 \\ +\ 58.54 \\ \hline \end{array}$$

3)
$$\begin{array}{r} 58.56 \\ +\ 12.10 \\ \hline \end{array}$$

6)
$$\begin{array}{r} 162.05 \\ -\ 83.65 \\ \hline \end{array}$$

✎ **Solve.**

7) ___ $+ 5.0 = 9.08$

10) $32.12 -$ ___ $= 12.07$

8) $7.06 +$ ___ $= 24.6$

11) ___ $+ 0.156 = 3.054$

9) $21.9 -$ ___ $= 6.9$

12) ___ $- 5.33 = 21.98$

Multiplying and Dividing Decimals

✍ **Find each product**

1) $\begin{array}{r} 1.5 \\ \times\, 0.16 \\ \hline \end{array}$

4) $\begin{array}{r} 3.19 \\ \times\, 21.5 \\ \hline \end{array}$

7) $\begin{array}{r} 5.0 \\ \times\, 1.4 \\ \hline \end{array}$

2) $\begin{array}{r} 5.3 \\ \times\, 1.9 \\ \hline \end{array}$

5) $\begin{array}{r} 9.3 \\ \times\, 11.5 \\ \hline \end{array}$

8) $\begin{array}{r} 23.8 \\ \times\, 10 \\ \hline \end{array}$

3) $\begin{array}{r} 0.06 \\ \times\, 2.5 \\ \hline \end{array}$

6) $\begin{array}{r} 3.01 \\ \times\, 2.1 \\ \hline \end{array}$

9) $\begin{array}{r} 21.5 \\ \times\, 10 \\ \hline \end{array}$

✍ **Find each quotient.**

10) $25.7 \div 0.5$

11) $67.2 \div 4$

12) $61.75 \div 1.9$

13) $18.0 \div 1.2$

14) $12.4 \div 10$

15) $2.2 \div 100$

16) $1.88 \div 100$

17) $55.1 \div 100$

18) $0.1 \div 100$

19) $0.25 \div 10$

Converting Between Fractions, Decimals and Mixed Numbers

✎ Convert fractions to decimals.

1) $\dfrac{25}{100}$

4) $\dfrac{4}{12}$

7) $\dfrac{12}{48}$

2) $\dfrac{4}{10}$

5) $\dfrac{5}{16}$

8) $\dfrac{20}{25}$

3) $\dfrac{3}{8}$

6) $\dfrac{60}{100}$

9) $\dfrac{26}{80}$

✎ Convert decimal into fraction or mixed numbers.

10) 0.25

14) 3.5

18) 0.15

11) 8.25

15) 0.5

19) 0.07

12) 0.12

16) 3.6

20) 2.7

13) 0.75

17) 0.07

21) 2.5

Answers of Worksheets – Chapter 2

Simplifying Fractions

1) $\frac{11}{16}$

2) $\frac{6}{13}$

3) $\frac{3}{5}$

4) $\frac{2}{3}$

5) $\frac{2}{3}$

6) $\frac{1}{3}$

7) $\frac{7}{18}$

8) $\frac{12}{29}$

9) $\frac{1}{3}$

10) $\frac{1}{9}$

11) $\frac{7}{11}$

12) $\frac{14}{19}$

13) $5\frac{5}{8}$

14) $2\frac{12}{21}$

15) $9\frac{1}{7}$

16) $3\frac{3}{5}$

17) $1\frac{1}{2}$

18) $4\frac{2}{11}$

19) $1\frac{11}{14}$

20) $\frac{9}{10}$

21) $7\frac{1}{2}$

Factoring Numbers

1) 1, 2, 3,5,6,9,10,15,18,30,45,90

2) 1, 2,3,4,6, 12

3) 1,7, 49

4) 1, 2, 5, 10,20, 25, 50, 100

5) 1, 2, 5, 10, 25, 50

6) 1, 2, 4, 8, 16, 32, 64

7) 1, 2 , 17, 34

8) 1, 3,9,27

9) 1, 3,7,9, 21, 63

10) 1,2, 5,10,11,22, 55, 110

11) 1,2, 3,4,6,8,12,16,24,32,48, 96

12) 1, 2, 3, 4, 6, 8, 12, 16, 24, 48

13) $2 \times 2 \times 2 \times 5$

14) $2 \times 3 \times 5 \times 7$

15) $3 \times 5 \times 7$

16) $2 \times 2 \times 2 \times 3$

17) $2 \times 3 \times 7$

18) $2 \times 3 \times 11$

19) $2 \times 3 \times 13$

20) $3 \times 5 \times 11$

21) $5 \times 5 \times 5$

22) $2 \times 2 \times 2 \times 2 \times 2$

23) $2 \times 2 \times 3$

24) 23×1

25) $2 \times 2 \times 3 \times 5$

26) $2 \times 3 \times 3 \times 3$

Greatest Common Factor

1) 1

2) 12

3) 9

4) 3

5) 3

6) 11

7) 6

8) 10

9) 20

10) 7

11) 32

12) 45

13) 12

14) 15

15) 21

16) 25

17) 4

18) 15

Least Common Multiple

1) 36

2) 30

3) 120

4) 28

5) 96

6) 40

7) 420

8) 126

9) 156

10) 60

11) 72

12) 60

13) 72

14) 210

15) 378

16) 429

17) 42

18) 792

Divisibility Rules

1) 12   <u>2</u> <u>3</u> <u>4</u> 5 <u>6</u> 7 8 9 10

2) 24   <u>2</u> <u>3</u> <u>4</u> 5 <u>6</u> 7 <u>8</u> 9 10

3) 36   <u>2</u> <u>3</u> <u>4</u> 5 <u>6</u> 7 8 <u>9</u> 10

4) 18   <u>2</u> <u>3</u> 4 5 <u>6</u> 7 8 <u>9</u> 10

5) 30   <u>2</u> <u>3</u> 4 <u>5</u> <u>6</u> 7 8 9 <u>10</u>

6) 54   <u>2</u> <u>3</u> 4 5 <u>6</u> 7 8 <u>9</u> 10

7) 64   <u>2</u> 3 <u>4</u> 5 6 7 <u>8</u> 9 10

8) 42   <u>2</u> <u>3</u> 4 5 <u>6</u> <u>7</u> 8 9 10

9) 90   <u>2</u> <u>3</u> 4 <u>5</u> <u>6</u> 7 8 <u>9</u> <u>10</u>

10) 80 <u>2</u> 3 <u>4</u> <u>5</u> 6 7 <u>8</u> 9 <u>10</u>

11) 72 <u>2</u> <u>3</u> <u>4</u> 5 <u>6</u> 7 <u>8</u> <u>9</u> 10

12) 84 <u>2</u> <u>3</u> <u>4</u> 5 <u>6</u> <u>7</u> 8 9 10

Adding and Subtracting Fractions

1) $\frac{11}{12}$

2) $\frac{5}{6}$

3) $\frac{27}{28}$

4) $\frac{2}{5}$

5) $\frac{3}{4}$

6) $1\frac{2}{21}$

7) $1\frac{1}{4}$

8) 1

9) $\frac{23}{26}$

10) $\frac{3}{10}$

11) $\frac{2}{63}$

12) $\frac{8}{15}$

13) $\frac{8}{21}$

15) $\frac{5}{24}$

17) $\frac{1}{12}$

14) $\frac{1}{3}$

16) $\frac{5}{12}$

18) $\frac{11}{30}$

Multiplying and Dividing Fractions

1) $\frac{1}{3}$

9) $\frac{1}{3}$

16) $1\frac{1}{4}$

2) $\frac{2}{7}$

10) $1\frac{1}{2}$

17) $\frac{3}{4}$

3) $\frac{1}{6}$

11) $\frac{7}{3}$

18) $\frac{4}{5}$

4) $\frac{1}{9}$

12) $\frac{1}{9}$

19) $\frac{15}{16}$

5) 1

13) 0

20) $10\frac{1}{2}$

6) 0

14) $\frac{4}{5}$

21) $2\frac{2}{3}$

7) 8

15) $2\frac{1}{2}$

22) $\frac{5}{6}$

8) $1\frac{1}{3}$

Adding Mixed Numbers

1) 4

5) $3\frac{1}{2}$

9) $5\frac{7}{8}$

2) $4\frac{3}{4}$

6) $9\frac{1}{2}$

10) $10\frac{1}{9}$

3) $3\frac{10}{21}$

7) 7

11) $7\frac{1}{6}$

4) $5\frac{1}{6}$

8) $3\frac{11}{12}$

12) $5\frac{5}{14}$

Subtract Mixed Numbers

1) $3\frac{3}{14}$

5) 2

9) $1\frac{1}{5}$

2) $3\frac{11}{15}$

6) $2\frac{1}{3}$

10) $2\frac{2}{9}$

3) $2\frac{5}{14}$

7) $1\frac{5}{6}$

11) $4\frac{11}{20}$

4) $2\frac{1}{15}$

8) $3\frac{1}{6}$

12) $1\frac{1}{36}$

Multiplying Mixed Numbers

1) $1\frac{1}{6}$

4) $3\frac{3}{4}$

7) 4

2) $\frac{14}{15}$

5) $5\frac{5}{6}$

8) $15\frac{2}{5}$

3) $7\frac{7}{9}$

6) 2

9) $3\frac{4}{15}$

10) $5\frac{5}{6}$ 11) $8\frac{1}{3}$ 12) $9\frac{3}{5}$

Dividing Mixed Numbers

1) $1\frac{13}{15}$ 5) $\frac{33}{56}$ 9) $\frac{25}{33}$

2) $\frac{3}{5}$ 6) $\frac{5}{7}$ 10) $\frac{5}{7}$

3) $1\frac{49}{55}$ 7) 0 11) $\frac{25}{56}$

4) $\frac{6}{11}$ 8) $1\frac{3}{5}$ 12) $\frac{3}{5}$

Comparing Decimals

1) <   6) <   11) >   16) <

2) >   7) <   12) =   17) <

3) >   8) =   13) <   18) <

4) <   9) <   14) >   19) >

5) <   10) >   15) >   20) >

Rounding Decimals

1) 2.0   10) 8.7   19) 1.5

2) 1.0   11) 6.1   20) 25

3) 13   12) 12.3   21) 67.71

4) 5   13) 9.3   22) 173.2

5) 3   14) 10.07   23) 32.2

6) 0.1   15) 56   24) 4.1

7) 11.1   16) 59   25) 0.03

8) 14   17) 330   26) 10.5

9) 7.92   18) 92   27) 2.3

Adding and Subtracting Decimals

1) 54.8   5) 156.665   9) 15

2) 134.52   6) 78.4   10) 20.05

3) 70.66   7) 4.08   11) 2.898

4) 8.75   8) 17.54   12) 27.31

Multiplying and Dividing Decimals

1) 0.24   2) 10.07   3) 0.15

4) 68.585

5) 106.95

6) 6.321

7) 7

8) 238

9) 215

10) 51.4

11) 16.8

12) 32.5

13) 15

14) 1.24

15) 0.022

16) 0.0188

17) 0.551

18) 0.001

19) 0.025

Converting Between Fractions, Decimals and Mixed Numbers

1) 0.25

2) 0.4

3) 0.375

4) 0.333

5) 0.3125

6) 0.6

7) 0.25

8) 0.8

9) 0.325

10) $\frac{1}{4}$

11) $8\frac{1}{4}$

12) $\frac{3}{25}$

13) $\frac{3}{4}$

14) $3\frac{1}{2}$

15) $\frac{1}{2}$

16) $3\frac{3}{5}$

17) $\frac{7}{100}$

18) $\frac{15}{100}$

19) $\frac{7}{100}$

20) $\frac{27}{10}$

21) $2\frac{1}{2}$

Chapter 3: Proportion, Ratio, Percent

Topics that you'll learn in this chapter:

> ➤ Writing and Simplifying Ratios

> ➤ Create a Proportion

> ➤ Similar Figures

> ➤ Simple Interest

> ➤ Ratio and Rates Word Problems

> ➤ Percentage Calculations

> ➤ Converting Between Percent, Fractions, and Decimals

> ➤ Percent Problems

> ➤ Markup, Discount, and Tax

"Do not worry about your difficulties in mathematics. I can assure you mine are still greater." – Albert Einstein

Writing and Simplifying Ratios

✎ **Express each ratio as a rate and unite rate.**

1) 80 dollars for 4 chairs.

4) 12 inches of snow in 24 hours

2) 125miles on 25 gallons of gas.

5) 14 dimes to 112 dimes

3) 147 miles on 7 hours

6) 30 feet out of 90 feet

✎ **Express each ratio as a fraction in the simplest form.**

7) 13 cups to 39 cups

10) 8 story books out of 32 books

8) 17 cakes out of 51 cakes

11) 12 gallons to 20 gallons

9) 35 red desks out of 125 desks

12) 11 miles out of 121 miles

✎ **Reduce each ratio.**

1) 49: 14

7) 18: 99

13) 15: 45

2) 35: 25

8) 64: 72

14) 18: 81

3) 16: 36

9) 70: 40

15) 32: 56

4) 4: 60

10) 16: 24

16) 10: 55

5) 8: 64

11) 14: 22

17) 12: 24

6) 22: 55

12) 5: 45

18) 23:115

Create a Proportion

✍ Create proportion from the given set of numbers

1) 3, 2, 9, 6

4) 20, 10, 200, 1

7) 24, 7, 21, 8

2) 5, 11, 25, 55

5) 4, 2, 16, 32

8) 15, 12, 30, 24

3) 49, 7, 12, 84

6) 4, 18, 12, 6

9) 9, 27, 81, 3

Similar Figures

✍ Each pair of figures is similar. Find the missing side.

1)
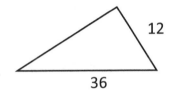

2)

3)
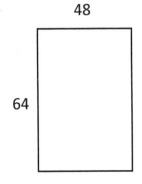
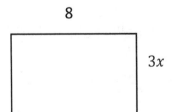

Ratio and Rates Word Problems

✍ **Solve.**

1) In Peter's class, 21 of the students are tall and 9 are short. In Elise's class 56 students are tall and 24 students are short. Which class has a higher ratio of tall to short students?

2) In a party, 8 soft drinks are required for every 35guests. If there are 560 guests, how many soft drinks is required?

3) The price of 5 bananas at the first Market is $1.05. The price of 7of the same bananas at second Market is $1.07. Which place is the better buy?

4) You can buy 6 cans of green beans at a supermarket for $3.50. How much does it cost to buy 42 cans of green beans?

5) The bakers at a Bakery can make 110 bagels in 4 hours. How many bagels can they bake in 6 hours? What is that rate per hour?

Percentage Calculations

Calculate the percentages.

1) 75% of 45

2) 50% of 66

3) 90% of 58

4) 25% of 88

5) 5% of 100

6) 80% of 60

7) 15% of 45

8) 18% of 90

9) 20% of 70

10) 12% of 25

11) 25% of 75

12) 75% of 18

13) 30% of 50

14) 10% of 85

15) 5% of 90

16) 50% of 10

Solve.

17) What percentage of 60 is 6

18) 6.76 is what percentage of 52?

19) 17 is what percentage of 85?

20) Find what percentage of 96 is 24.

Percent Problems

✏️ **Solve each problem.**

1) 52% of what number is 13?

2) What is 15% of 9 inches?

3) What percent of 185.6 is 23.2?

4) 24 is 72% of what?

5) 35 is what percent of 70?

6) 10 is 200% of what?

7) 14 is what percent of 70?

8) 26% of 100 is what number?

9) Mia require 50% to pass. If she gets 250 marks and falls short by 90 marks, what were the maximum marks she could have got?

10) Jack scored 14 out of 70 marks in mathematics, 9 out of 10 marks in history and 56 out of 100 marks in science. In which subject his percentage of marks is the best?

Markup, Discount, and Tax

✏️ **Find the selling price of each item.**

1) Cost of a chair: $20, markup: 30%, discount: 10%, tax: 10%

2) Cost of computer: $1,600.00, markup: 65%

3) Cost of a pen: $3.20, markup: 50%, discount: 15%, tax: 5%

4) Cost of a puppy: $1,800, markup: 40%, discount: 10%

Simple Interest

Use simple interest to find the ending balance.

1) $1,200 at 15% for 3 years.

2) $320,000 at 2.85% for 7 years.

3) $1,500 at 2.25% for 12 years.

4) $12,500 at 6.2% for 4 years.

5) $31,000 at 1.5% for 10 months.

6) Emily puts $6,000 into an investment yielding 3.25% annual simple interest; she left the money in for 3 years. How much interest does Sara get at the end of those 3 years?

7) A new car, valued at $42,000, depreciates at 7.5% per year from original price. Find the value of the car 6 years after purchase.

8) $880 interest is earned on a principal of $2,200 at a simple interest rate of 4% interest per year. For how many years was the principal invested?

Converting Between Percent, Fractions, and Decimals

✎ **Converting fractions to decimals**

1) $\dfrac{23}{10}$ 4) $\dfrac{20}{50}$ 7) $\dfrac{3}{10}$

2) $\dfrac{2}{20}$ 5) $\dfrac{3}{60}$ 8) $\dfrac{13}{26}$

3) $\dfrac{7}{100}$ 6) $\dfrac{15}{10}$ 9) $\dfrac{8}{100}$

✎ **Write each decimal as a percent.**

10) 2.15   15) 0.002

11) 0.26   16) 0.08

12) 1.09   17) 0.2

13) 0.51   18) 3.25

14) 0.025   19) 1.01

Answers of Worksheets – Chapter 3

Writing Ratios

1) $\frac{80 \text{ dollars}}{4 \text{ books}}$, 20.00 dollars per chair

2) $\frac{125 \text{ miles}}{25 \text{ gallons}}$, 5 miles per gallon

3) $\frac{147 \text{ miles}}{7 \text{ hours}}$, 21 miles per hour

4) $\frac{12'' \text{ of snow}}{24 \text{ hours}}$, 0.5 inches of snow per hour

5) $\frac{14 \text{ dimes}}{112 \text{ dimes}}$, $\frac{1}{8}$ per dime

6) $\frac{30 \text{ feet}}{90 \text{ feet}}$, $\frac{1}{3}$ per foot

7)

8) $\frac{1}{3}$

9) $\frac{7}{25}$

10) $\frac{1}{4}$

11) $\frac{3}{5}$

12) $\frac{1}{11}$

Reduce each Ratio

1) 7: 2

2) 7: 5

3) 4: 9

4) 1: 15

5) 1: 8

6) 2: 5

7) 2: 11

8) 8: 9

9) 7: 4

10) 2: 3

11) 7: 11

12) 1: 9

13) 1: 3

14) 2: 9

15) 4: 7

16) 2: 11

17) 1: 2

18) 1: 5

Create a Proportion

1) 2: 6 = 3: 9

2) 5: 25 = 11: 55

3) 7: 49 = 12: 84

4) 1: 10 = 20: 200

5) 2: 16=4: 32

6) 4: 12 =6: 18

7) 8: 24 =7: 21

8) 12: 24 =15: 30

9) 3: 27 =9: 81

Similar Figures

1) 6

2) 4

3) 2

Ratio and Rates Word Problems

1) The ratio for both classes is equal to 7 to 3.

2) 128

3) The price at the second Market is a better buy.

4) $24.5

5) 165, the rate is 27.5 per hour.

Percentage Calculations

1) 33.75	6) 48	11) 18.75	16) 5
2) 33	7) 6.75	12) 13.5	17) 10%
3) 52.2	8) 16.2	13) 15	18) 13%
4) 22	9) 14	14) 8.5	19) 20%
5) 5	10) 3	15) 4.5	20) 25%

Percent Problems

1) 25	5) 50%	9) 680
2) 60	6) 5	10) history
3) 12.5	7) 20%	
4) 33.33	8) 26	

Markup, Discount, and Tax

1) $25.74	3) $4.284
2) $2,640	4) $2,268

Simple Interest

1) $1740	4) $15600	7) $23,100
2) $383,840.00	5) $31,387.50	8) 10 years
3) $1,905.00	6) $585.00	

Converting Between Percent, Fractions, and Decimals

1) 2.3	8) 0.5	15) 0.2%
2) 0.01	9) 0.08	16) 8%
3) 0.07	10) 215%	17) 20%
4) 0.4	11) 26%	18) 325%
5) 0.05	12) 109%	19) 101%
6) 1.5	13) 51%	
7) 0.3	14) 2.5%	

Chapter 4: Exponents and Radicals

Topics that you'll learn in this chapter:

- ➢ Multiplication Property of Exponents

- ➢ Division Property of Exponents

- ➢ Powers of Products and Quotients

- ➢ Zero, Negative Exponents and Bases

"Mathematics is no more computation than typing is literature." – John Allen Paulos

Multiplication Property of Exponents

✍ **Simplify.**

1) $4^3 \times 4^2$

2) $2 \cdot 2^2 \cdot 2^3$

3) $2^4 \cdot 2$

4) $8x^2 \cdot x$

5) $15x^7 \cdot x$

6) $3x \cdot x^3$

7) $2x^5 \cdot 5x^4$

8) $5x^2 \cdot 3x^2 y^2$

9) $6y^5 \cdot 8xy^2$

10) $5xy^3 \cdot 4x^3 y^2$

11) $(2x^3)^2$

12) $2x^4 y \cdot 3x^2 y^2$

13) $6x \cdot 5y^4 x^2 \cdot 2yx^3$

14) $(x^3)^3$

15) $(3x^2)^3$

16) $2x^3 y^5 \cdot 2xy^2$

Division Property of Exponents

✍ **Simplify.**

1) $\dfrac{4^3}{4}$

2) $\dfrac{51}{51^{14}}$

3) $\dfrac{5^2}{5^3}$

4) $\dfrac{3^4}{3^1}$

5) $\dfrac{x}{x^7}$

6) $\dfrac{42x^2}{6x^2}$

7) $\dfrac{3x^{-3}}{12x^{-1}}$

8) $\dfrac{81x^5}{9x^3}$

9) $\dfrac{3x^4}{4x^5}$

10) $\dfrac{21x}{3x^2}$

11) $\dfrac{3x}{7x^4}$

12) $\dfrac{2x^2}{3x^6}$

13) $\dfrac{18x^3}{10x^5}$

14) $\dfrac{14x}{7y^5}$

15) $\dfrac{2xy^5}{x^5y}$

16) $\dfrac{2x^2}{5x}$

17) $\dfrac{8x^2y}{x^3}$

18) $\dfrac{3x^4}{7x^5y^4}$

19) $\dfrac{yx^3}{5yx^3}$

20) $\dfrac{3x^4}{2x^5}$

21) $\dfrac{x^7}{3x^7}$

Powers of Products and Quotients

✎ Simplify.

1) $(2x^2)^3$

2) $(xy)^2$

3) $(5x^3)^2$

4) $(9x^3)^2$

5) $(4x^2y^3)^2$

6) $(5x^2y^3)^2$

7) $(2xy^2)^3$

8) $(2x^3y)^4$

9) $(7x^4y^8)^2$

10) $(10x)^3$

11) $(x^5)^3$

12) $(8x^{10}y^2)^3$

13) $(9x^2x^2)^2$

14) $(2x^2\ 8x)^2$

15) $(11x^9y^3)^2$

16) $(6x^5\ y^3)^2$

17) $(3\ x^3\ )^5$

18) $(7x^3)^2$

19) $(2x\ 4y^4)^2$

20) $(6xy)^3$

21) $(15x^2y^3)^2$

Zero and Negative Exponents

✎ Evaluate the following expressions.

1) 4^{-2}

2) 5^{-2}

3) 6^{-2}

4) 3^{-4}

5) 10^{-1}

6) 33^{-1}

7) 6^{-1}

8) 3^{-2}

9) 9^{-2}

10) 4^{-1}

11) 5^{-3}

12) 2^{-5}

13) 11^{-2}

14) 2^{-4}

15) 7^{-2}

16) 2^{-3}

17) 2^{-2}

18) 9^{-1}

19) 4^{-3}

20) 10^{-4}

21) $\left(\frac{2}{3}\right)^{-2}$

22) $\left(\frac{1}{3}\right)^{-2}$

23) $\left(\frac{1}{2}\right)^{-3}$

24) $\left(\frac{6}{5}\right)^{-2}$

25) 11^{-2}

26) 3^{-1}

Negative Exponents and Negative Bases

✎ Simplify.

1) 7^{-1}

2) $-2x^{-2}$

3) $\frac{x}{x^{-5}}$

4) $-\frac{a^{-2}}{b^{-1}}$

5) $\frac{7}{x^{-5}}$

6) $\frac{2b}{-5c^{-2}}$

7) $\frac{2n^{-1}}{12p^{-2}}$

8) $\frac{8b^{-4}}{3c^{-2}}$

9) $89xy^{-2}$

10) $\left(\frac{1}{3}\right)^{-2}$

11) $\left(\frac{6}{7}\right)^{-2}$

12) $\left(\frac{x}{4yz}\right)^{-2}$

Writing Scientific Notation

✎ Write each number in scientific notation.

1) 25×10^3

2) 12

3) 0.0015

4) 54,000

5) 0.0051

6) 666

7) 0.0076

8) 2900

9) 100,000

10) 3,600,000

11) 60,000,000

12) 150

13) 0.108

14) 20

15) 260

16) 1,000,000

17) 0.00015

18) 0.3

Square Roots

✎ Find the value each square root.

1) $\sqrt{25}$

2) $\sqrt{1,600}$

3) $\sqrt{100}$

4) $\sqrt{121}$

5) $\sqrt{4}$

6) $\sqrt{225}$

7) $\sqrt{10,000}$

8) $\sqrt{16}$

9) $\sqrt{64}$

10) $\sqrt{36}$

11) $\sqrt{484}$

12) $\sqrt{49}$

13) $\sqrt{0.01}$

14) $\sqrt{81}$

15) $\sqrt{961}$

16) $\sqrt{400}$

17) $\sqrt{1}$

18) $\sqrt{196}$

19) $\sqrt{144}$

20) $\sqrt{169}$

21) $\sqrt{676}$

Answers of Worksheets – Chapter 4

Multiplication Property of Exponents

1) 4^5

2) 2^6

3) 2^5

4) $8x^3$

5) $15x^8$

6) $3x^4$

7) $10x^9$

8) $15x^4y^2$

9) $48xy^7$

10) $20x^4y^5$

11) $4x^6$

12) $6x^6y^3$

13) $60x^6y^5$

14) x^9

15) $27x^6$

16) $4x^4y^7$

Division Property of Exponents

1) 4^2

2) $\dfrac{1}{51^{13}}$

3) $\dfrac{1}{5}$

4) 3^3

5) $\dfrac{1}{x^6}$

6) 7

7) $\dfrac{1}{4x^2}$

8) $9x^2$

9) $\dfrac{3}{4x}$

10) $\dfrac{7}{x}$

11) $\dfrac{3}{7x^3}$

12) $\dfrac{2}{3x^4}$

13) $\dfrac{9}{5x^2}$

14) $\dfrac{2x}{y^5}$

15) $\dfrac{2y^4}{x^4}$

16) $\dfrac{2x}{5}$

17) $\dfrac{8y}{x}$

18) $\dfrac{3}{7xy^4}$

19) $\dfrac{1}{5}$

20) $\dfrac{3}{2x}$

21) $\dfrac{1}{3}$

Powers of Products and Quotients

1) $8x^6$

2) x^2y^2

3) $25x^6$

4) $81x^6$

5) $16x^4y^6$

6) $25x^4y^6$

7) $8x^3y^6$

8) $8x^{12}y^4$

9) $49x^8y^{16}$

10) $1{,}000x^3$

11) x^{15}

12) $512x^{30}y^6$

13) $81x^8$

14) $256x^6$

15) $121x^{18}y^6$

16) $36x^{10}y^6$

17) $243x^{15}$

18) $49x^6$

19) $64x^2y^8$

20) $216x^3y^3$

21) $225x^4y^6$

Zero and Negative Exponents

1) $\frac{1}{16}$

2) $\frac{1}{25}$

3) $\frac{1}{36}$

4) $\frac{1}{81}$

5) $\frac{1}{10}$

6) $\frac{1}{33}$

7) $\frac{1}{6}$

8) $\frac{1}{9}$

9) $\frac{1}{81}$

10) $\frac{1}{4}$

11) $\frac{1}{125}$

12) $\frac{1}{32}$

13) $\frac{1}{121}$

14) $\frac{1}{16}$

15) $\frac{1}{49}$

16) $\frac{1}{8}$

17) $\frac{1}{4}$

18) $\frac{1}{9}$

19) $\frac{1}{64}$

20) $\frac{1}{10,000}$

21) $\frac{9}{4}$

22) 9

23) 8

24) $\frac{25}{36}$

25) $\frac{1}{121}$

26) $\frac{1}{3}$

Negative Exponents and Negative Bases

1) $\frac{1}{7}$

2) $\frac{2}{x^2}$

3) x^5

4) $-\frac{b^1}{a^2}$

5) $7x^5$

6) $-2\frac{bc^2}{5}$

7) $\frac{p^2}{6n}$

8) $\frac{8c^2}{3b^4}$

9) $\frac{89x}{y^2}$

10) 9

11) $\frac{49}{36}$

12) $\frac{16y^2z^2}{x^2}$

Writing Scientific Notation

1) 2.5×10^4

2) 1.2×10^1

3) 1.5×10^{-3}

4) 5.4×10^4

5) 5.1×10^{-3}

6) 6.66×10^2

7) 7.6×10^{-3}

8) 2.9×10^3

9) 1×10^5

10) 3.6×10^6

11) 6×10^7

12) 1.5×10^2

13) 1.08×10^{-1}

14) 2×10^1

15) 2.6×10^2

16) 1×10^6 17) 1.5×10^{-4} 18) 3×10^{-1}

Square Roots

1) 5	8) 4	15) 31
2) 40	9) 8	16) 20
3) 10	10) 6	17) 1
4) 11	11) 22	18) 14
5) 2	12) 7	19) 12
6) 15	13) 0.1	20) 13
7) 100	14) 9	21) 26

Chapter 5: Algebraic Expressions

Topics that you'll learn in this chapter:

- ➤ Expressions and Variables

- ➤ Simplifying Variable and Polynomial Expressions

- ➤ Translate Phrases into an Algebraic Statement

- ➤ The Distributive Property

- ➤ Evaluating One and two Variable

- ➤ Combining like Terms

"Without mathematics, there's nothing you can do. Everything around you are mathematics. Everything around you are numbers." – Shakuntala Devi

Translate Phrases into an Algebraic Statement

✎ **Write an algebraic expression for each phrase.**

1) fifteen subtracted from a number.

2) The quotient of seventeen and a number.

3) A number increased by fifty.

4) A number divided by -21.

5) The difference between sixty –three and a number.

6) Threefold a number decreased by 45.

7) seven times the sum of a number and -21.

8) The quotient of 90 and the product of a number and -8.

The Distributive Property

✎ **Use the distributive property to simply each expression.**

1) $4(9 - 3x)$

2) $-(-8 - 4x)$

3) $(-5x - 1)(-2)$

4) $(-3)(2x - 4)$

5) $4(5 + 3x)$

6) $(-9x + 10)3$

7) $(-4 - 5x)(-3)$

8) $(-15)(2x + 3)$

9) $(-2)(3x - 1) + 4(3x + 2)$

10) $(-2x)(-3 + 2x) - 3x(1 - 5x)$

11) $2(-6x - 3) + 5(1 - 2x)$

12) $(-3)(x + 4) - (5 + 2x)$

Evaluating One Variable

✐Simplify each algebraic expression.

1) $5x + 4, x = 1$

2) $x + (-4), x = -6$

3) $-10x + 8, x = -2$

4) $\left(-\frac{36}{x}\right) - 10 + 2x, x = 6$

5) $\frac{36}{x} - 3, x = 3$

6) $(-10) - \frac{x}{4} + 4x, x = -8$

7) $15 + 6x - 3, x = -1$

8) $(-5) + \frac{x}{8}, x = 64$

9) $\left(-\frac{24}{x}\right) - 10 + 5x, x = 4$

10) $(-4) + \frac{4x}{9}, x = 81$

Evaluating Two Variables

✐Simplify each algebraic expression.

1) $5a - (5 - b),$

   $a = 2, b = 3$

2) $5x + 3y - 6 + 3y,$

   $x = 3, y = 1$

3) $\left(-\frac{27}{x}\right) + 4 + 3y,$

   $x = 3, y = 5$

4) $(-4)(-3a - 5b),$

   $a = 3, b = 4$

5) $7x + 10 - 5y,$

   $x = 3, y = 6$

6) $18 + 3(-x - 4y),$

   $x = 2, y = 5$

7) $12x + 2y,$

   $x = 5, y = 10$

8) $x \times 6 \div 3y,$

   $x = 6, y = 1$

Expressions and Variables

✎ **Simplify each expression.**

1) $10(-3 - 8x), x = 4$

2) $-3(5 - 8x) - 6x, x = 1$

3) $2x - 8x, x = 2$

4) $x + 12x, x = 6$

5) $20 - 5x + 10x + 5, x = 3$

6) $15(5x + 3), x = 0$

7) $20(4 - x) - 9, x = 2$

8) $20x - 8x - 10, x = 5$

9) $6x + 9y, \ x = 4, y = 2$

10) $6x - 2x, x = 8,$

11) $7(-3x + 11) + 9, x = 7,$

12) $12x - 20x + 25, x = 2,$

13) $6x - 5x - 9, x = 9$

14) $(-3)(-x - 6y), x = 5, y = 2$

15) $18x + 3 - 16 \, y, x = 3, y = 5$

16) $(-10)(-5x - 7y), x = 5, y = 5$

Combining like Terms

✍ **Simplify each expression.**

1) $-8(-5x + 1)$

2) $6(-2 + 4x)$

3) $-8 - 14x + 16x + 3$

4) $9x - 7x - 15 + 18$

5) $(-9)(12x - 21) + 31$

6) $2(4x + 9) + 12x$

7) $4(-2x - 17) + 14(3x + 1)$

8) $(9x - 5y)7 + 25y$

9) $4.5x^3 \times (-8x)$

10) $-19 - 15x^2 + 12x^2$

11) $8 + 15x^2 + 12$

12) $15(-2x - 1) + 28$

13) $9x^2 + 4x + 3x^2$

14) $14x^2 - 11x^2 + 10x$

15) $4x^2 - 8x - 11x$

16) $(-8)(15x - 10)$

17) $9x + 6(3 - 5x)$

18) $-12x + 5(20x - 8)$

19) $6(11x + 0.5)$

20) $-30(x + 1) + 20x$

21) $5x - 16y + 6x + 13y - 23x$

22) $5(-2x + 5y) + 20x - 18y$

23) $(-5x) - 2 + 5x + 3$

24) $11(2x + 1) + 13(x - 1)$

Simplifying Polynomial Expressions

✍ **Simplify each polynomial.**

1) $(2x^2 + 4) - (9 + 5x^2)$

2) $(25x^3 - 12x^2) - (6x^2 - 9x^3)$

3) $14x^5 - 15x^6 + 2x^5 - 16x^6 + x^6$

4) $(-2x^5 + 20 - 4x) + (9x^4 + 10x + 6x^5)$

5) $13x^2 - 15x^4 + 12x^3 + 20x^4 + 13x^3$

6) $-6x^2 + 15x^2 + 17x^3 + 16 - 32$

7) $15x^3 + 12 + 2x^2 - 5x - 10x$

8) $24x^2 - 16x^3 - 4x(2x^2 + 3x)$

9) $(21x^4 - 10x) - (2x - x^4)$

10) $(15x^3 + 20x^4) - (12x^4 - 3x^3)$

11) $(15 + 12x^3) + (3x^3 + 5)$

12) $(7x^2 - 9) + (x^2 - 8x^3)$

Answers of Worksheets – Chapter 5

Translate Phrases into an Algebraic Statement

1) $x - 15$

2) $\dfrac{17}{x}$

3) $x + 50$

4) $-\dfrac{x}{21}$

5) $63 - x$

6) $3x - 45$

7) $7(x + (-21))$

8) $-\dfrac{90}{8x}$

The Distributive Property

1) $-12x + 36$

2) $4x + 8$

3) $10x + 2$

4) $-6x + 12$

5) $12x + 20$

6) $-27x + 30$

7) $15x + 12$

8) $-30x - 45$

9) $6x + 10$

10) $11x^2 + 3x$

11) $-22x - 1$

12) $-5x - 17$

Evaluating One Variable

1) 9

2) -10

3) 28

4) -4

5) 9

6) -40

7) 6

8) 3

9) 4

10) 32

Evaluating Two Variables

1) 8

2) 15

3) 10

4) 116

5) 1

6) -48

7) 80

8) 12

Expressions and Variables

1) -350

2) 3

3) -12

4) 78

5) 40

6) 45

7) 31

8) 50

9) 42

10) 32

11) -61

12) 9

13) 0

14) 51

15) -23

16) 600

Combining like Terms

1) $40x - 8$

2) $24x - 12$

3) $2x - 5$

4) $2x + 3$

5) $220 - 108x$

6) $20x + 18$

7) $34x - 54$

8) $63x - 10y$

9) $-36x^4$

10) $-3x^2 - 19$

11) $15x^2 + 20$

12) $-30x + 13$

13) $12x^2 + 4x$

14) $3x^2 + 10x$

15) $4x^2 - 19x$

16) $-120x + 80$

17) $-21x + 18$

18) $88x - 40$

19) $66x + 3$

20) $-10x - 30$

21) $-12x - 3y$

22) $10x + 7y$

23) 1

24) $35x - 2$

Simplifying Polynomial Expressions

1) $-3x^2 - 5$

2) $34x^3 - 18x^2$

3) $-30x^6 + 16x^5$

4) $4x^5 + 9x^4 + 6x + 20$

5) $5x^4 + 25x^3 + 13x^2$

6) $17x^3 + 9x^2 - 16$

7) $15x^3 + 2x^2 - 15x + 12$

8) $-24x^3 + 12x^2$

9) $22x^4 - 12x$

10) $8x^4 + 18x^3$

11) $15x^3 + 20$

12) $-8x^3 + 8x^2 - 9$

Chapter 6: Equations and Inequalities

Topics that you'll learn in this chapter:

- ➢ One, Two, and Multi – Step Equations

- ➢ Graphing Single– Variable Inequalities

- ➢ One, Two, and Multi – Step Inequalities

- ➢ Solving Systems of Equations by Substitution and Elimination

- ➢ Finding Slope and Writing Linear Equations

- ➢ Graphing Lines Using Slope– Intercept and Standard Form

- ➢ Graphing Linear Inequalities

- ➢ Finding Midpoint and Distance of Two Points

"The study of mathematics, like the Nile, begins in minuteness but ends in magnificence." – Charles Caleb Colton

One–Step Equations

✍ Solve each equation.

1) $x + 4 = 16$

2) $48 = (-2) + x$

3) $5x = (-105)$

4) $(-8) = (8x)$

5) $(-2) = 14 + x$

6) $5 + x = 6$

7) $2x + 3 = (-7)$

8) $28 = x + 7$

9) $(-15) + x = (-15)$

10) $12x = (-36)$

11) $x + 8 = (-27)$

12) $x - 4 = (-44)$

13) $(-20) = x - 45$

14) $(-8x) = 88$

15) $(-16) = (2x)$

16) $x + 13 = 55$

17) $25x = 100$

18) $64 = (-8x)$

19) $12x = 48$

20) $15x = 120$

Two–Step Equations

✎ **Solve each equation.**

1) $4(2 + 2x) = 8$

2) $(-5)(x - 3) = 25$

3) $(-5)(2x - 5) = (-15)$

4) $4(9 + 3x) = -12$

5) $6(2x + 1) = 30$

6) $2(x + 2) = 42$

7) $2(12 + 6x) = 60$

8) $(-10)(5x) = 100$

9) $4(3x + 3) = 24$

10) $\frac{x - 5}{3} = 4$

11) $18 = \frac{x + 6}{2}$

12) $88 = (-4)(x - 5)$

13) $\frac{2x}{3} - 10 = 2$

14) $-18 = 7 + \frac{x}{4}$

15) $\frac{4 + 2x}{12} = 3$

16) $(-6 + 12x) = 90$

17) $(-2x) + 15 = 45$

18) $\frac{x + 3}{12} = 6$

19) $\frac{3x + 9}{4} = (-9)$

20) $(-4) + \frac{2x}{7} = 16$

Multi–Step Equations

✎ **Solve each equation.**

1) $8 - 2x = 28$

2) $-10 = -(x + 7)$

3) $2x - 17 = (-x) + 1$

4) $-2x = (-3x) - 8$

5) $5(14 + 2x) + 3x = -x$

6) $x - 11 = x - 5 + 2x$

7) $15 + 2x = (-25) - 2x + 3x$

8) $-3(x - 3x) = 40 - 4x$

9) $24 + 8x + x = (-x + 4)$

10) $-8(1 + 5x) = 152$

11) $16 = (-3x) - 1 + 2$

12) $15 = 2x - 4x + 3$

13) $2(x + 5x) = 144$

14) $-9 = (-x + 1) - 9x$

15) $x + 6 = (-x + 5x)$

16) $4x - 5x = 4x + 15$

17) $5 + x = -(x - 5)$

18) $-7 = (2 + 3x)$

19) $22 + x = -3(2 + x)$

20) $x + 2 = x - 2x + 8$

Graphing Single–Variable Inequalities

Draw a graph for each inequality.

1) $2 \geq x$
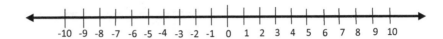

2) $x < 3$

3) $5 \geq x$

4) $x \geq -2$

5) $x > 0$

6) $-1.5 < x$

One–Step Inequalities

 Solve each inequality and graph it.

1) $2x + 3 \geq 7$

2) $x - 3 \leq 2$

3) $-2x + 3 \geq -1$

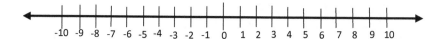

4) $x - 3 > -8$

5) $-3x \geq 12$

6) $5x - 1 < 9$

7) $x + 3 > -3$

Two–Step Inequalities

✎ Solve each inequality and graph it.

1) $x - 4 \leq 4$

2) $x + 4 \geq 5$

3) $3x - 2 \leq 7$

4) $5x + 2 < 12$

5) $x + 7 \geq 9$

6) $3x - 3 \leq 3$

7) $7x - 4 < 3$

8) $8 + x \leq 13$

9) $2x + 7 \leq 11$

10) $10x - 16 < 4$

11) $6x - 11 \geq 1$

12) $2x + 3 < 15$

13) $6x + 4 \geq 28$

14) $11 + 2x < 21$

15) $8 + 2x \geq 28$

16) $9 + 4x < 25$

Multi–Step Inequalities

✎ Solve each inequality.

1) $-(x + 3) + 8 < 25$

2) $\frac{3x + 1}{2} \leq 5$

3) $\frac{x - 4}{3} > 7$

4) $4(x - 2) \leq 8$

5) $\frac{x}{3} + \frac{1}{3} < 2$

6) $\frac{x + 4}{5} > 3$

Solving Systems of Equations by Substitution

✎ Solve each system of equation by substitution.

1) $-x + 5y = -4$

$$x - 3y = 8$$

2) $2x + 3y = -6$

$$-2x - y = 8$$

3) $x + 2y = -5$

$$5x - 10y = 5$$

4) $y = -x + 5$

$$3x - y = -3$$

5) $3x = 6$

$$10y = 4x + 2$$

6) $3x + 2y = 2$

$$x + 4y = -6$$

7) $4x + y = 3$

$$2x + 4y = -2$$

8) $4y = 2x + 3$

$$x - 4y = -2$$

Solving Systems of Equations by Elimination

✍ Solve each system of equation by elimination.

1) $-5x + y = -5$

$$-y = -6x + 6$$

2) $-6x - 2y = -2$

$$2x - 3y = 8$$

3) $5x - 4y = 8$

$$-6x + y = -21$$

4) $10x - 4y = -24$

$$-x - 20y = -18$$

5) $25x + 3y = -13$

$$12x - 6y = -36$$

6) $x - 8y = -7$

$$6x + 4y = 10$$

7) $-6x + 16y = 4$

$$5x + y = 11$$

8) $2x - 3y = -10$

$$4x + 6y = -20$$

Systems of Equations Word Problems

✎Solve.

1) A school of 220 students went on a field trip. They took 20 vehicles, some vans and some minibuses. Find the number of vans and the number of minibuses they took if each van holds 5 students and each minibus hold 15 students.

2) The sum of two numbers is 28. Their difference is 12. Find the numbers.

3) A farmhouse shelters 20 animals, some are pigs, and some are gooses. Altogether there are 64 legs. How many of each animal are there?

4) The sum of the digits of a certain two–digit number is 15. Reversing it's increasing the number by 9. What is the number?

5) The difference of two numbers is 16. Their sum is 32. Find the numbers.

Linear Equations

Find the slope of the line through each pair of points.

1) $(3, 1), (2, 4)$

2) $(-3, 4), (-1, 6)$

3) $(4, 4), (6, -6)$

4) $(-1, 8), (5, -4)$

5) $(12, -3), (7, -3)$

6) $(11, -14), (13, -4)$

7) $(-4, 6), (-10, 0)$

8) $(10, 12), (2, -4)$

9) $(12, -1), (0, 5)$

10) $(-1, 7), (-2, 2)$

11) $(11, 12), (1, 22)$

12) $(36, 9), (6, -11)$

Write the slope–intercept form of the equation of the line through the given points.

1) Through: $(2, 3), (4, 2)$

2) Through: $(8, -3), (6, 7)$

3) Through: $(0.5, 4), (2.5, 4.4)$

4) Through: $(4, -2), (2.5, 1)$

5) Through: $(-1, 0.7), (-2.3, 2)$

6) Through: $(4, 7), (2, 10)$

7) Through: $(2.7, 6), (4.5, 6)$

8) Through: $(-3, 2), (1, 6)$

9) Through: $(1, -2), (8, 12)$

10) Through: $(1.5, 6), (-2.5, 2)$

11) Through: $(2, 0), (-3, -2)$

12) Through: $(9, 4), (1, -4)$

Graphing Lines of Equations

✎ Sketch the graph of each line

1) $y = 3x - 2$

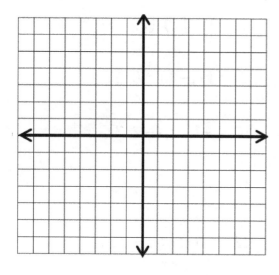

2) $y = 2x + 3$

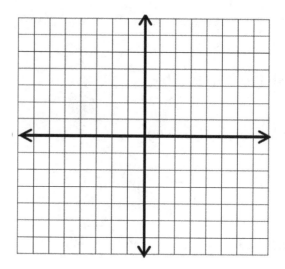

3) $-2x = y + 5$

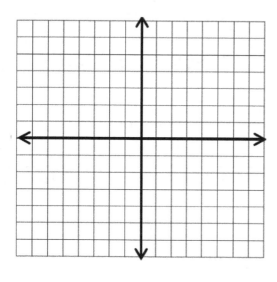

4) $4x + y = 2$

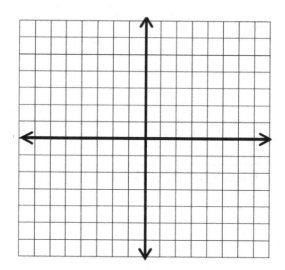

Graphing Linear Inequalities

✎Sketch the graph of each linear inequality.

1) $2y + 8x \geq 4$

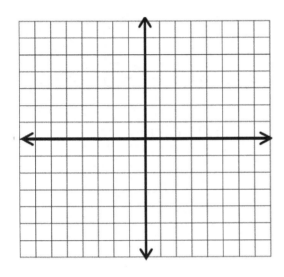

2) $-x + 2y \leq 4$

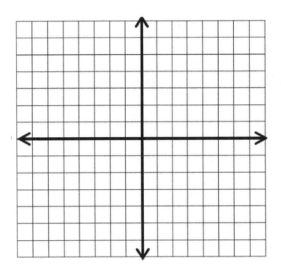

3) $2x + \frac{1}{2}y < 2$

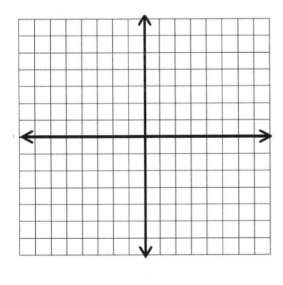

4) $-\frac{1}{3}x + y < 2$

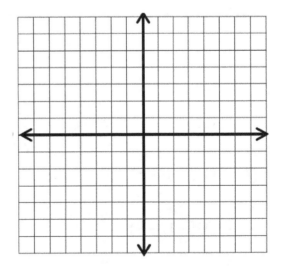

Finding Distance of Two Points

✏️ Find the midpoint of the line segment with the given endpoints.

1) $(1.5, -1), (0.5, -1)$

2) $(4, 1), (-1, -5)$

3) $(0, 3), (4, -9)$

4) $(5, 2), (1, 5)$

5) $(-2, 0), (3, -4)$

6) $(1, -2), (1.5, 5)$

7) $(1.25, 2.5), (-0.25, -1.5)$

8) $(1, 0.5), (-2, 0.5)$

9) $(-3, 6), (-1, -2)$

10) $(1, 7), (2, 1)$

11) $(3.2, 4), (1, -4)$

12) $(7, 8), (3, 2)$

✏️ Find the distance between each pair of points.

1) $(3, 4), (2, -1)$

2) $(6, -1), (2, 3)$

3) $(2, 5), (-2, 5)$

4) $(0, -4), (-5, 1)$

5) $(3, -2), (-1, -5)$

6) $(10, 4), (-1, -7)$

7) $(2, 5), (2, 4)$

8) $(5, 8), (-3, -4)$

9) $(8, 3), (9, -6)$

10) $(-2, 3), (4, 7)$

11) $(8, 5), (-1, 0)$

12) $(4, -1), (0, 1)$

Answers of Worksheets – Chapter 6

One–Step Equations

1) 12	6) 1	11) – 35	16) 42
2) 50	7) – 5	12) – 40	17) 4
3) – 21	8) 21	13) –25	18) – 8
4) –1	9) 0	14) -11	19) 4
5) – 16	10) – 3	15) -8	20) 8

Two–Step Equations

1) 0	6) 10	11) 30	16) 8
2) -2	7) 3	12) – 17	17) -15
3) 4	8) -2	13) 18	18) 69
4) -4	9) 1	14) -100	19) – 15
5) 2	10) 17	15) 16	20) 70

Multi–Step Equations

1) –10	8) 4	15) 2
2) 3	9) –2	16) -3
3) 6	10) – 4	17) 0
4) –8	11) – 5	18) – 3
5) – 5	12) –6	19) – 7
6) –3	13) 12	20) 3
7) –40	14) 1	

Graphing Single–Variable Inequalities

 1) $2 \geq x$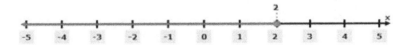

 2) $x < 3$

3) $5 \geq x$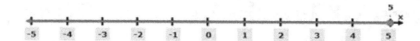

4) $x \geq -2$

5) $x > 0$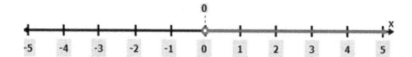

6) $-1.5 < x$

One–Step Inequalities

1)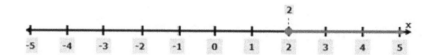

2)

3)

4)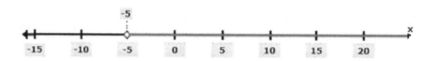

5)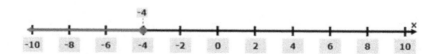

6)

7)

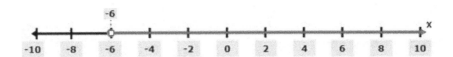

Two–Step inequalities

1) $x \leq 8$

5) $x \geq 2$

9) $x \leq 2$

13) $x \geq 4$

2) $x \geq 1$

6) $x \leq 2$

10) $x < 2$

14) $x < 5$

3) $x \leq 3$

7) $x < 1$

11) $x \geq 2$

15) $x \geq 10$

4) $x < 2$

8) $x \leq 5$

12) $x < 6$

16) $x < 4$

Multi–Step inequalities.

1) $x > -20$

3) $x > 2\,5$

5) $x < 5$

2) $x \leq 3$

4) $x \leq 4$

$x > 11$

Solving Systems of Equations by Substitution

1) $(14, 2)$

4) $(\frac{1}{2}, \frac{9}{2})$

8) $(-1, \frac{1}{4})$

2) $(-\frac{9}{2}, 1)$

5) $(2, 1)$

3) $(-2, -\frac{3}{2})$

6) $(2, -2)$

7) $(1, -1)$

Solving Systems of Equations by Elimination

1) $(1, 0)$

4) $(-2, 1)$

7) $(2, 1)$

2) $(1, -2)$

5) $(-1, 4)$

8) $(-5, 0)$

3) $(4, 3)$

6) $(1, 1)$

Systems of Equations Word Problems

1) There are 8 van and 12 minibuses.

4) 78

2) 8 and 20

5) 24 and 8.

3) There are 12 pigs and 8 gooses.

Finding Slope

1) -3

3) -5

5) 0

7) 1

2) 1

4) -2

6) 5

8) 2

9) $-\frac{1}{2}$ 10) 5   11) -1 12) $\frac{2}{3}$

Writing Linear Equations

1) $y = -\frac{1}{2}x + 4$

2) $y = -5x + 37$

3) $y = \frac{1}{5}x + \frac{39}{10}$

4) $y = -2x + 6$

5) $y = -x - 0.3$

6) $y = -\frac{3}{2}x + 13$

7) $y = 6$

8) $y = x + 5$

9) $y = 2x - 4$

10) $y = x + 4.5$

11) $y = \frac{2}{5}x - \frac{4}{5}$

12) $y = x - 5$

Graphing Lines Using Slope–Intercept Form

1)

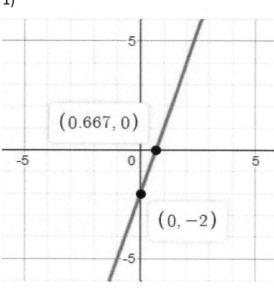

2)

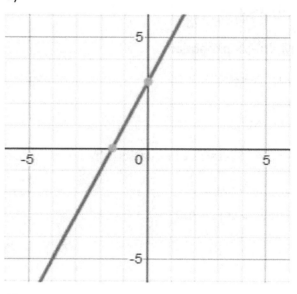

3)

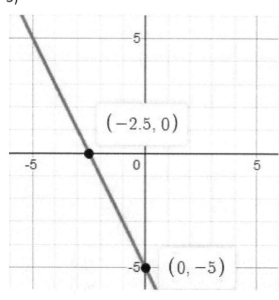

4)

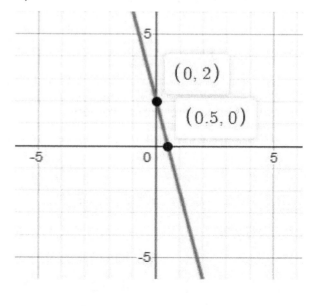

Graphing Linear Inequalities

1)

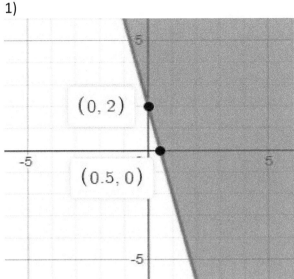

2)

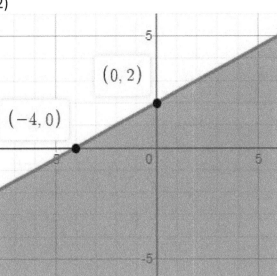

3)

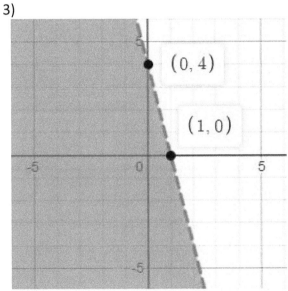

4)

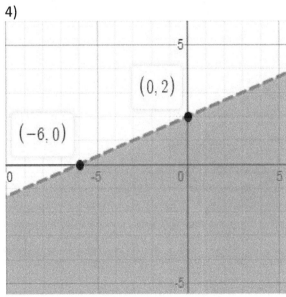

Finding Midpoint

1) $(1, -1)$	4) $(3, 3.5)$	7) $(0.5, 0.5)$	10) $(1.5, 4)$
2) $(1.5, -2)$	5) $(0.5, -2)$	8) $(-0.5, 0.5)$	11) $(2.1, 0)$
3) $(2, -3)$	6) $(1.25, 1.5)$	9) $(-2, 2)$	12) $(5, 5)$

Finding Distance of Two Points

1) 5.09	4) 7.07	7) 1	10) 7.21
2) 5.656	5) 5	8) 14.42	11) 10.29
3) 4	6) 15.56	9) 9.055	12) 4.47

Chapter 7: Polynomials

Topics that you'll learn in this chapter:

- ➢ Classifying Polynomials

- ➢ Writing Polynomials in Standard Form

- ➢ Simplifying Polynomials

- ➢ Adding and Subtracting Polynomials

- ➢ Multiplying and Dividing Monomials

- ➢ Multiplying a Polynomial and a Monomial

- ➢ Multiplying Binomials

- ➢ Factoring Trinomials

- ➢ Operations with Polynomials

"Mathematics – the unshaken Foundation of Sciences, and the plentiful Fountain of Advantage to human affairs." – Isaac Barrow

Classifying Polynomials

Name each polynomial by degree and number of terms.

1) -5

2) $x + 1$

3) $3x - 2$

4) $8x^6 - 7$

5) $3x^2 - x$

6) $5x^2 - 6x^3$

7) $-10x^4$

8) $17x^5$

9) $-10 + 4x^2 + 2x$

10) $11x^6 - 9$

11) $7x^6 + 5x^2 - 4x^4$

12) $-8x^4 + 3x^3 - 2x^2 - 3x$

13) $2x - 12x^2 + 5x^3 - 4x^4$

14) $12x^6 + 7x^5 - 3x^2$

Write each polynomial in standard form

1) $12x^4 + x - 4x^3$

2) $x + x^3 - 9$

3) $12 - x^3 - 3x^5 + 9x^4$

4) $x^2 + 12 - x$

5) $x(x + 2) - (3x^5 + 2)$

6) $x^2 + 13x^5 + x^3 - 4x$

7) $10 + x^3 + x^3 - 3x^5 + 2x^3$

8) $x(x + x^5 + x^3 + 6)$

9) $x^5 + 2x^3(x^2 + 2)$

10) $x + (x + 2)$

11) $x^4 + 2x^5 + x^3$

12) $(x - 5)(x + 5)$

13) $x(1 + 2x^3 + 2x)$

14) $2 - 8x + 2x^2$

Simplifying Polynomials

✍ **Simplify each expression.**

1) $-3x^2 + x^5 + 7x^5 - 2x^2 + 6$

2) $18x^5 - 3x^5 + 7x^2 - 15x^5 + 4$

3) $x(x^3 + 9) - 6(8 + x^2)$

4) $x(x^2 + 2x^3) - x^3 + x$

5) $4 - 17x^2 + 30x^2 - 17x^2 + 26$

6) $4x^2 - 8x + 3x^3 + 15x - 20x$

7) $(x - 6)(x - x^2 + 5)$

8) $(x - 5)(x + 5)$

9) $(7x^3 + 28x^2 + 28x) \div 7(2x + x^2)$

10) $(12x + 9x^2 + 4) \div (3x + 2)$

11) $(x^4 - x) + (4x^2 - 3x^4)$

12) $x(x^2 + x + 3)$

13) $(4x + 5)(4x - 5)$

14) $(x^2 - 3x) + (12 + 8x^2 + 18x)$

Adding and Subtracting Polynomials

🖊️**Simplify each expression.**

1) $(x^3 + 6) - (6 + 3x^3)$

2) $(x^2 + 8) + (7x^2 - 8)$

3) $(2x^2 + x^3) - (5x^2 + 1)$

4) $(6x^2 - 4x) + (3x - 6x^2 + 1)$

5) $(x - 2x^3) - (4x^3 + 4)$

6) $(2x^3 + 2x^2) - (2x^2 - x^3 + 2)$

7) $(4x^2 - 3) + (x^2 - x^3)$

8) $(x^3 + 13x^4) - (13x^4 + 3x^3)$

9) $(-x^4 + 2x^5 + 3x^3) + (14x^3 + 16x^4)$

10) $(10x^3 - 6x^6 - x + 5) + (-10x^3 + 11x^6 - 9x)$

11) $(42 + 8x^4 - 4x^2) + (2x^4 + 2x^2) - (22 - 5x^4)$

12) $(-3x^3 - 3x + 2) + (3x + 8x^4 - 10) + (x^2 + x^3 + 10)$

Multiplying Monomials

🖊️**Simplify each expression.**

1) $2xy^2 \times 3z^2$

2) $3xyz \times 5x^2y$

3) $4pq^3 \times (-3p^3q)$

4) $s^3t^2 \times 2st^5$

5) $5p^3 \times (-2p^2)$

6) $-2p^2r \times 6pr^3$

7) $(-a)(-4a^6b)$

8) $2u^2v^3 \times (-8u^3v^3)$

9) $6u^3 \times (2u)$

10) $-5y^2 \times 4x^2y$

11) $13y^2z^2 \times (-y^4z)$

12) $8a^3c^2 \times 5abc^2$

Multiply and Divide Monomials

✎ Simplify.

1) $(x^3y^2)(42y^4)$

2) $\dfrac{100x^5y^6}{25x^6y^{11}}$

3) $(8x^4)(12x^5)$

4) $\dfrac{75x^{16}y^{10}}{5x^6y^7}$

5) $(-2x^{-3}y^2)^2$

6) $\dfrac{15x^{12}y^5}{5x^9y^2}$

7) $(11x^2y^4)(4x^9y^{10})$

8) $\dfrac{50x^4y^7}{25x^3y^7}$

9) $(2x^{-3}y^4)^2$

10) $\dfrac{-21x^8y^{13}}{3x^6y^6}$

11) $(2x^{-2}y^{-1})(-4x^{-2}y^3)$

12) $\dfrac{121x^6y^9}{11x^3y^7}$

Multiply a Polynomial and a Monomial

✎ Find each product.

1) $3(2x-2y)$

2) $5x(4x-y)$

3) $-2x(x+5)$

4) $11(3x+7)$

5) $10x(5x-2y)$

6) $4(3x-5y)$

7) $2x(3x^3-5x+4)$

8) $-4x(2+4xy)$

9) $3(2x^2-8x+3)$

10) $-3x^2(3x^2+5)$

11) $x^2(4x^3-2xy+xy^2)$

12) $3x^2(3-5x)$

13) $2x^2(x^4+5x-9)$

14) $4x(7x^2-5y+y^2)$

Multiply Binomials

✎ **Multiply.**

1) $(2x - 2)(x + 3)$

2) $(4x + 2)(2x + 1)$

3) $(x + 3)(x + 4)$

4) $(x^2 + 5)(x^2 - 5)$

5) $(2x - 3)(x + 4)$

6) $(2x - 6)(x + 7)$

7) $(x - 2)(3x - 4)$

8) $(2x - 5)(x + 4)$

9) $(x + 10)(x - 10)$

10) $(x - 3)(3x + 4)$

11) $(x - 5)(2x + 8)$

12) $(x - 1)(4x + 2)$

13) $(2x - 1)(2x + 1)$

14) $(x + 5)(x - 3)$

15) $(x + 4)(x + 7)$

16) $(x + 2)(4x - 1)$

Factor Trinomials

✎ **Factor each trinomial.**

1) $x^2 - 12x + 27$

2) $x^2 + 5x - 24$

3) $x^2 + 13x + 30$

4) $x^2 - 81$

5) $2x^2 + 12x - 14$

6) $x^2 + 2x - 8$

7) $2x^2 + 3x + 1$

8) $2x^2 + 2x - 4$

9) $9x^2 + 3x - 2$

10) $x^2 + 15x + 56$

11) $16x^2 + 12xy + 2y^2$

12) $3x^2 - 14x + 8$

13) $2x^2 - 8x + 8$

14) $5x^2 + 12x + 4$

Operations with Polynomials

✎Find each product.

1) $x^2(3x - 2)$

2) $2x^2(5x - 3)$

3) $-x(5x - 3)$

4) $x^2(-3x + 9)$

5) $5(7x + 3)$

6) $8(3x + 8)$

7) $5(10x + 4)$

8) $-3x^5(x - 3)$

9) $5(3x^2 - x + 2)$

10) $4(x^2 - 2x + 3)$

11) $10(6x^2 + 5x - 2)$

12) $3x(2x^2 + 2x + 7)$

13) $(7x + 1)(x - 2)$

14) $(x + 11)(3x - 1)$

15) $(3x + 2)(3x - 2)$

16) $(2x - 4)(x + 2)$

Answers of Worksheets – Chapter 7

Classifying Polynomials

1) Constant monomial

2) Linear binomial

3) Linear binomial

4) Sixth degree binomial

5) Quadratic binomial

6) cubic binomial

7) Quartic monomial

8) Quantic binomial

9) Quadratic trinomial

10) Sixth degree binomial

11) Sixth degree trinomial

12) Quartic polynomial with four terms

13) Quartic polynomial with four terms

14) Sixth degree trinomial

Writing Polynomials in Standard Form

1) $12x^4 - 4x^3 + x$

2) $x^3 + x - 9$

3) $-3x^5 + 9x^4 - x^3 + 12$

4) $x^2 - x + 12$

5) $-3x^5 + x^2 + 2x - 2$

6) $13x^5 + x^3 + x^2 - 4x$

7) $-3x^5 + 4x^3 + 10$

8) $x^6 + x^4 + x^2 + 6x$

9) $2x^6 + x^5 + 4x^3$

10) $2x + 2$

11) $2x^5 + x^4 + x^3$

12) $x^2 - 25$

13) $2x^4 + 2x^2 + x$

14) $2x^2 - 8x + 2$

Simplifying Polynomials

1) $8x^5 - 5x^2 + 6$

2) $7x^2 + 4$

3) $x^4 - 6x^2 + 9x - 48$

4) $2x^4 + x$

5) $-4x^2 + 30$

6) $3x^3 + 4x^2 - 13x$

7) $-x^3 + 7x^2 - x - 30$

8) $x^2 - 25$

9) $x + 2$

10) $3x + 2$

11) $-2x^4 + 4x^2 - x$

12) $x^3 + x^2 + 3x$

13) $16x^2 - 25$

14) $9x^2 + 15x + 12$

Adding and Subtracting Polynomials

1) $-2x^3$

2) $8x^2$

3) $x^3 - 3x^2 + 1$

4) $-x + 1$

5) $-6x^3 + x - 4$

6) $3x^3 - 2$

7) $-x^3 + 5x^2 - 3$

8) $-2x^3$

9) $2x^5 + 15x^4 + 17x^3$

10) $5x^6 - 10x + 5$

11) $5x^4 - 2x^2 + 20$

12) $8x^4 - 2x^3 + x^2 + 2$

Multiply Monomials

1) $6xy^2z^2$

2) $15x^3y^2z$

3) $-12p^4q^4$

4) $2s^4t^{10}$

5) $-10p^5$

6) $-12p^3r^4$

7) $4a^7b$

8) $-16u^5v^6$

9) $12u^4$

10) $-20x^2y^3$

11) $-13y^6z^3$

12) $40a^4bc^4$

Multiply and Divide Monomials

1) $42x^3y^6$

2) $4x^{-1}y^{-5}$

3) $96x^9$

4) $15x^{10}y^3$

5) $4x^{-6}y^4$

6) $3x^3y^3$

7) $44x^{11}y^{14}$

8) $2x$

9) $4x^{-6}y^8$

10) $-7x^2y^7$

11) $-8x^{-4}y^2$

12) $11x^3y^2$

Multiply a Polynomial and a Monomial

1) $6x - 6y$

2) $20x^2 - 5xy$

3) $-2x^2 - 10$

4) $33x + 77$

5) $50x^2 - 20xy$

6) $12x - 20y$

7) $6x^4 - 10x^2 + 8x$

8) $-16x^2y - 8x$

9) $6x^2 - 24x + 9$

10) $-9x^4 - 15x^2$

11) $4x^5 - 2x^3y + y^2x^3$

12) $9x^2 - 15x^3$

13) $2x^6 + 10x^3 - 18x^2$

14) $28x^3 - 20xy + 4xy^2$

Multiplying Binomials

1) $2x^2 + 4x - 6$

2) $8x^2 + 8x + 2$

3) $x^2 + 7x + 12$

4) $x^4 - 25$

5) $2x^2 + 5x - 12$

6) $2x^2 + 8x - 42$

7) $3x^2 - 10x + 8$

8) $2x^2 + 3x - 20$

9) $x^2 - 100$

10) $3x^2 - 5x - 12$

11) $2x^2 - 2x - 40$

12) $4x^2 - 2x - 2$

13) $4x^2 - 1$

14) $x^2 + 2x - 15$

15) $x^2 + 11x + 28$

16) $4x^2 + 7x - 2$

Factoring Trinomials

1) $(x - 3)(x - 9)$

2) $(x + 8)(x - 3)$

3) $(x + 10)(x + 3)$

4) $(x + 9)(x - 9)$

5) $(x + 7)(2x - 2)$

6) $(x - 2)(x + 4)$

7) $(2x + 1)(x + 1)$

8) $(2x - 2)(x + 2)$

9) $(3x - 1)(3x + 2)$

10) $(x + 7)(x + 8)$

11) $(4x + y)(4x + 2y)$

12) $(x - 4)(3x - 2)$

13) $(2x - 4)(x - 2)$

14) $(x + 2)(5x + 2)$

Operations with Polynomials

1) $3x^3 - 2x^2$

2) $10x^3 - 6x^2$

3) $-5x^2 + 3x$

4) $-3x^3 + 9x^2$

5) $35x + 15$

6) $24x + 64$

7) $50x + 20$

8) $-3x^6 + 9x^5$

9) $15x^2 - 5x + 10$

10) $4x^2 - 8x + 1\ 2$

11) $60x^2 + 50x - 20$

12) $6x^3 + 6x^2 + 21x$

13) $7x^2 - 13x - 2$

14) $3x^2 + 32x - 11$

15) $9x^2 - 4$

16) $2x^2 - 8$

Chapter 8: Geometry

Topics that you'll learn in this chapter:

➢ The Pythagorean Theorem

➢ Area of Triangles and Trapezoids

➢ Area and Circumference of Circles

➢ Area and Perimeter of Polygons

➢ Area of Squares, Rectangles, and Parallelograms

➢ Volume of Cubes, Rectangle Prisms, and Cylinder

➢ Surface Area of Cubes, Rectangle Prisms, and Cylinder

"Mathematics is, as it were, a sensuous logic, and relates to philosophy as do the arts, music, and plastic art to poetry." — K. Shegel

The Pythagorean Theorem

✍ Do the following lengths form a right triangle?

1)

5
3
4

2)

13   √290
11

3)

12
9
25

✍ Find each missing length to the nearest tenth.

4)
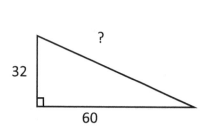

32   ?
60

5)

72
?
35

6)
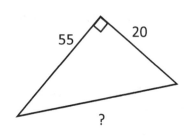

55   20
?

Angles

✎ **What is the value of** x **in the following figures?**

1)

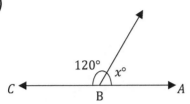

2)

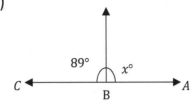

3)

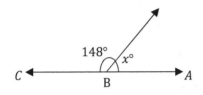

4)

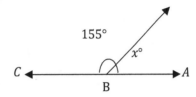

5)

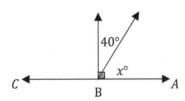

6)

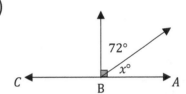

✎ *Solve.*

7) Six supplement peer to each other angles have equal measures. What is the measure of each angle? _____

8) The measure of an angle is one fourth the measure of its complementary. What is the measure of the angle? _____

Area of Triangles

✎ Find the area of each.

1)

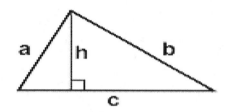

c = 15 mi

h = 4 mi

2)

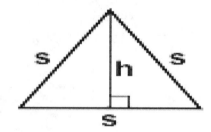

s = 6 m

h = 5.2 m

3)

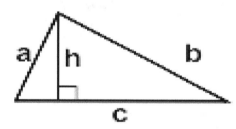

a = 9.5 m

b = 25 m

c = 18 m

h = 9 m

4)

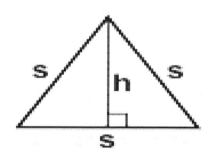

s = 8 m

h = 6.93 m

Area of Trapezoids

✎ Calculate the area for each trapezoid.

1)

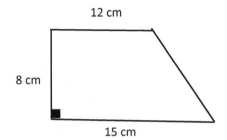

12 cm

8 cm

15 cm

2)

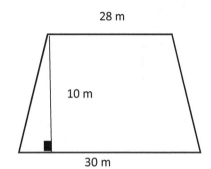

28 m

10 m

30 m

3)

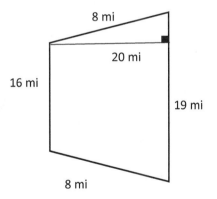

8 mi

20 mi

16 mi

19 mi

8 mi

4)

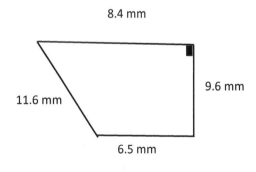

8.4 mm

11.6 mm

9.6 mm

6.5 mm

Area and Perimeter of Polygons

✎ Find the area and perimeter of each

1)

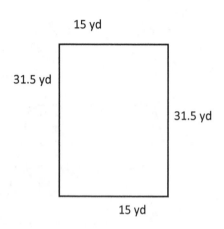

15 yd

31.5 yd

31.5 yd

15 yd

2)

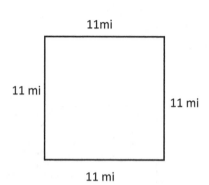

11mi

11 mi

11 mi

11 mi

3)

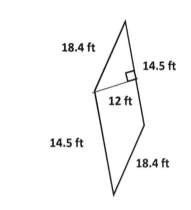

18.4 ft

14.5 ft

12 ft

14.5 ft

18.4 ft

4)

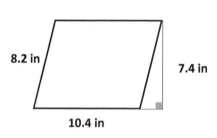

8.2 in

7.4 in

10.4 in

5)

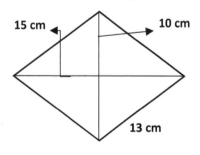

15 cm

10 cm

13 cm

6)

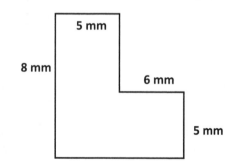

5 mm

8 mm

6 mm

5 mm

✎ **Find the perimeter of each shape.**

7)

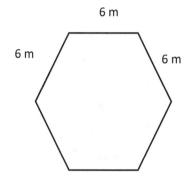

6 m

6 m   6 m

8)

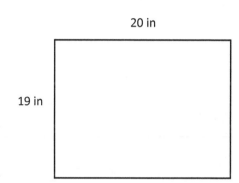

11mm

11 mm

9)

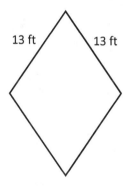

13 ft   13 ft

10)

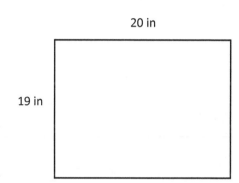

20 in

19 in

11)

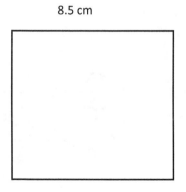

8.5 cm

12)

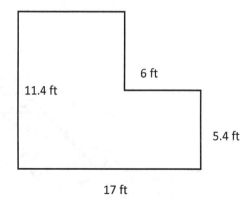

6 ft

11.4 ft

5.4 ft

17 ft

Area and Circumference of Circles

Find the area and circumference of each. (π = 3.14)

1)

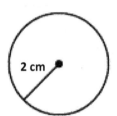

2)

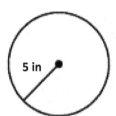

3)

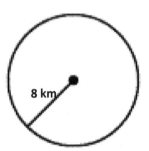

4)

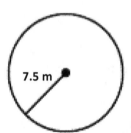

5)

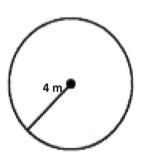

6)

7)

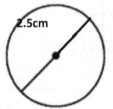

8)

Volume of Cubes

Find the volume of each.

1)

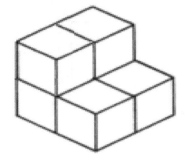

2)

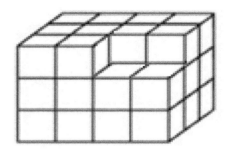

3)

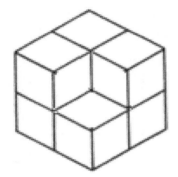

4)

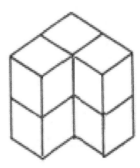

5)

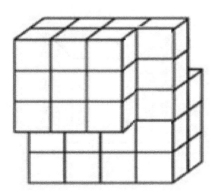

6)

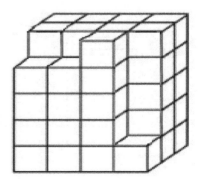

Volume of Rectangle Prisms

✎ Find the volume of each of the rectangular prisms.

1)

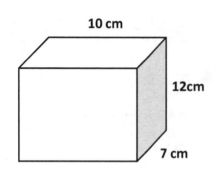

2)

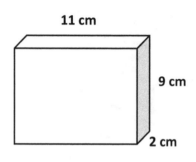

3)

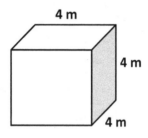

4)

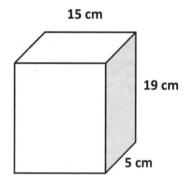

5)

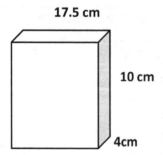

6)

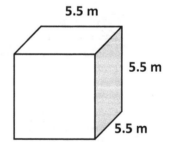

Surface Area of Cubes

✍ Find the surface of each cube.

1)

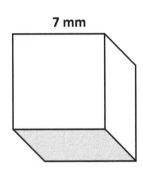

7 mm

2)

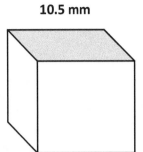

10.5 mm

3)

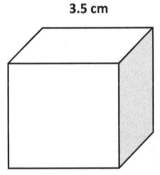

3.5 cm

4)

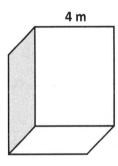

4 m

5)

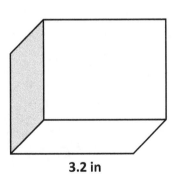

3.2 in

6)

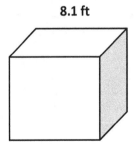

8.1 ft

Surface Area of a Rectangle Prism

✏️ Find the surface of each prism.

1)

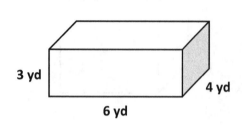

3 yd

4 yd

6 yd

2)

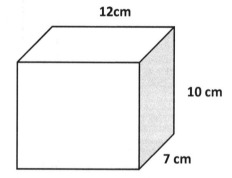

1.02 mm

1.5 mm

0.5 mm

3)

2.5 in

9.5 in

4 in

4)

12cm

10 cm

7 cm

Volume of a Cylinder

✎ **Find the volume of each cylinder.** ($\pi = 3.14$)

1)

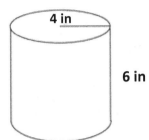

4 in

6 in

2)

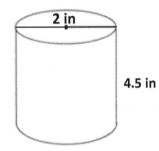

7 m

10 m

3)

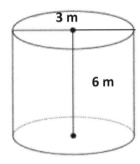

3 m

6 m

4)

2 in

4.5 in

5)

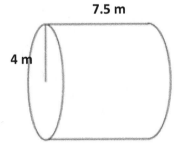

7.5 m

4 m

6)

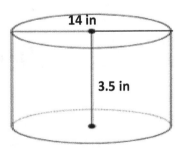

14 in

3.5 in

Surface Area of a Cylinder

✎ **Find the surface of each cylinder.** ($\pi = 3.14$)

1)

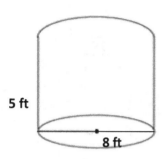

5 ft

8 ft

2)

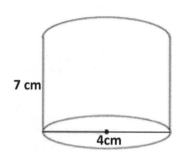

7 cm

4cm

3)

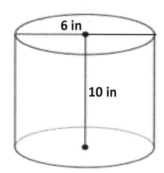

6 in

10 in

4)

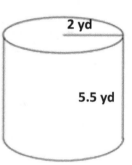

2 yd

5.5 yd

5)

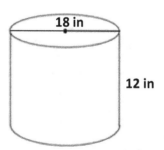

18 in

12 in

6)

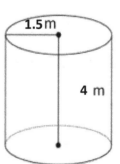

1.5 m

4 m

Answers of Worksheets – Chapter 8

The Pythagorean Theorem

1) yes

2) yes

3) no

4) 68

5) 62.92

6) 58.52

Angles

1) 60°

2) 91°

3) 32°

4) 25°

5) 50°

6) 18°

7) 30°

8) 18°

Area of Triangles

1) 30 mi^2

2) 15.6 m^2

3) 81 m^2

4) 27.72m^2

Area of Trapezoids

1) 108 cm^2

2) 290 m^2

3) 350 mi^2

4) 71.52 mm^2

Area of Squares, Rectangles, and Parallelograms

1) Area: 472.5 m^2, Perimeter: 93m

2) Area: 121 mm^2, Perimeter: 44mm

3) Area: 174 ft^2, Perimeter: 65.8 ft

4) Area: 76.96 in^2, Perimeter: 37.2in

5) Area: 75cm^2, Perimeter 52 cm

6) Area: 70 mm^2, Perimeter:38 mm

7) P: 36 m

8) P: 44 mm

9) P: 52 ft

10) P: 78 in

11) P: 34 cm

12) P: 56.8 ft

Area and Circumference of Circles

1) Area: 12.56 cm^2, Circumference: 12.56 cm.

2) Area: 78.5 in^2, Circumference: 31.4 in.

3) Area: 200.96 km^2, Circumference: 50.24 km.

4) Area: 176.625 m^2, Circumference: 47.1 m.

5) Area: 50.24 m^2, Circumference: 25.12 m

6) Area: 78.5 cm^2, Circumference: 31.4 cm.

7) Area: 4.906 cm^2, Circumference: 7.85 cm.

8) Area: 1.766 in^2, Circumference: 4.71 in.

Volumes of Cubes

1) 6

2) 34

3) 7

4) 6

5) 41

6) 54

Volume of Rectangle Prisms

1) 840 cm^3

2) 198 cm^3

3) 64 m^3

4) 1,425 cm^3

5) 700 cm^3

6) 166.375 cm^3

Surface Area of a Cube

1) 294 mm^2

2) 661.5 mm^2

3) 73.5 cm^2

4) 96 m^2

5) 61.44 in^2

6) 393.66 ft^2

Surface Area of a Rectangle Prism

1) 108 yd^2

2) 5.58 mm^2

3) 143.5 in^2

4) 548 cm^2

Volume of a Cylinder

1) 301.44 cm^3

2) 1538.6cm^3

3) 42.39 m^3

4) 14.13 m^3

5) 376.8 m^3

6) 538.51 m^3

Surface Area of a Cylinder

1) 226.08 ft^2

2) 113.04 cm^2

3) 224.92 in^2

4) 94.2 yd^2

5) 1,186.92 in^2

6) 51.81m^2

Chapter 9: Statistics

Topics that you'll learn in this chapter:

➢ Mean, Median, Mode, and Range of the Given Data

➢ Box and Whisker Plots

➢ Bar Graph

➢ Stem– And– Leaf Plot

➢ The Pie Graph or Circle Graph

➢ Dot and Scatter Plots

➢ Probability of Simple Events

"The book of nature is written in the language of Mathematic" -Galileo

Mean and Median

✏️ **Find Mean and Median of the Given Data.**

1) 8, 10, 7, 3, 12

2) 4, 6, 9, 7, 5, 19

3) 5, 11, 1, 1, 8, 9, 20

4) 12, 4, 2, 7, 3, 2

5) 3, 5, 7, 4, 7, 8, 9

6) 5, 10, 4, 4, 9, 12, 9

7) 10, 4, 8, 5, 9, 6, 7, 19

8) 16, 3, 4, 3, 7, 6, 18

9) 22, 20, 5, 11, 32, 44, 71

10) 14, 8, 9, 5, 4, 13, 8, 10

11) 8, 15, 35, 66, 41, 21

12) 24, 23, 54, 38, 71, 81

✏️ **Solve.**

13) In a javelin throw competition, five athletics score 23, 45,53.53,13and 61 meters. What are their Mean and Median? _____

14) Eva went to shop and bought 7 apples, 4 peaches, 6 bananas, 3 pineapple and 4melons. What are the Mean and Median of her purchase?

_____

Mode and Range

✎ **Find Mode and Rage of the Given Data.**

1) 10, 12, 8, 8, 4, 1, 9

    Mode: _____ Range: _____

2) 4, 6, 4, 13, 2, 13, 19, 13

    Mode: _____ Range: _____

3) 8, 8, 7, 2, 7, 7, 5, 6, 5

    Mode: _____ Range: _____

4) 12, 9, 12, 6, 12, 9, 10

    Mode: _____ Range: _____

5) 2, 2, 4, 3, 2, 10, 8

    Mode: _____ Range: _____

6) 6, 1, 4, 20, 19, 2, 7, 1, 5, 1

    Mode: _____ Range: _____

7) 16, 35, 9, 7, 7, 5, 14, 13, 7

    Mode: _____ Range: _____

8) 7, 6, 6, 9, 16, 6, 7, 5

    Mode: _____ Range: _____

9) 12, 5, 6, 12, 4, 4, 6, 4, 5

    Mode: _____ Range: _____

10) 2, 5, 10, 5, 4, 5, 10, 10

    Mode: _____ Range: _____

11) 4, 11, 5, 3, 12, 12, 18, 2

    Mode: _____ Range: _____

12) 6, 3, 3, 9, 6, 16, 3, 10

    Mode: _____ Range: _____

✎ **Solve.**

13) A stationery sold 15 pencils, 26 red pens, 22 blue pens, 10 notebooks, 12 erasers, 22 rulers and 42 color pencils. What are the Mode and Range for the stationery sells?

    Mode: _____   Range: _____

14) In an English test, eight students score 24, 13, 17, 21, 19, 13, 13 and 17. What are their Mode and Range? _____

Times Series

🖎 **Use the following Graph to complete the table.**

Day	Distance (km)
1	
2	

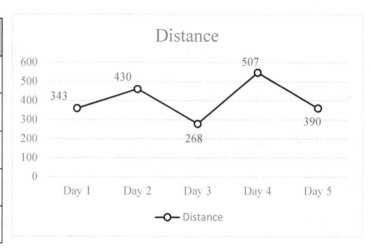

The following table shows the number of births in the US from 2007 to 2012 (in millions).

Year	Number of births (in millions)
2007	6.42
2008	6.45
2009	6.33
2010	5.9
2011	4.35
2012	4.35

Draw a time series for the table.

Box and Whisker Plot

✍ **Make box and whisker plots for the given data.**

1, 5, 20, 8, 3, 10, 13, 11, 14, 17, 18, 15, 23

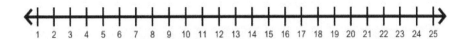

Bar Graph

✍ **Graph the given information as a bar graph.**

Day	Sale House
Monday	6
Tuesday	4
Wednesday	10
Thursday	5
Friday	2
Saturday	8
Sunday	1

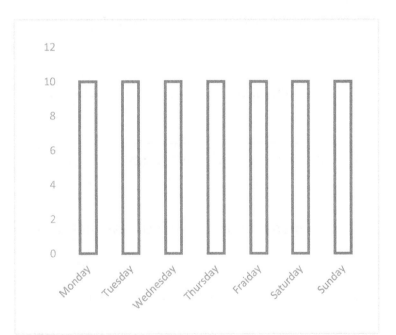

Dot plots

A survey of "How many pets each person owned?" has these results:

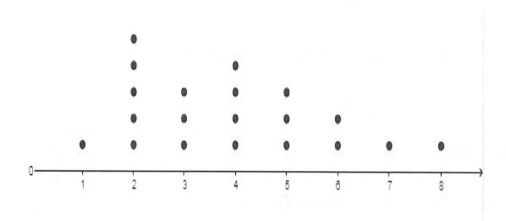

1) How many people have at least 3 pets?

2) How many people have 2 and 3 pets?

3) How many people have 4 pets?

4) How many people have 2 or less than 2 pets?

5) How many people have more than 7 pets?

Scatter Plots

✍ Construct a scatter plot.

x	1	2.5	3	3.5	4	5
y	4	3.5	4.5	2.5	8	2

Stem–And–Leaf Plot

✍ Make stem ad leaf plots for the given data.

1) 42, 14, 17, 21, 44, 24, 18, 47, 23, 24, 19, 12

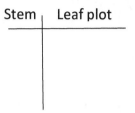

2) 10, 65, 14, 18, 69, 11, 33, 61, 66, 38, 15, 35

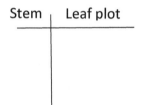

3) 122, 87, 99, 86, 100, 126, 92, 129, 88, 121, 91, 107

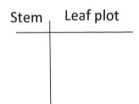

4) 60, 51, 119, 69, 72, 59, 110, 65, 77, 59, 65, 112, 71

Stem | Leaf plot

The Pie Graph or Circle Graph

Favorite Sports:

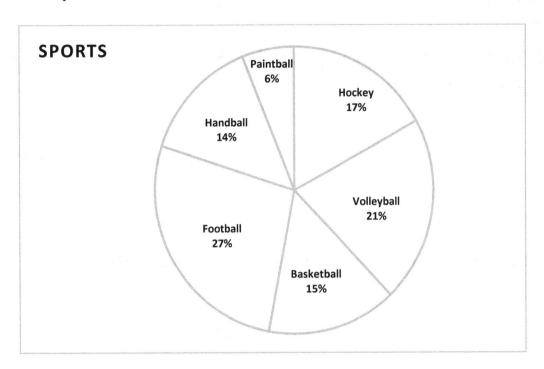

1) What percentage of pie graph is paintball?

2) What percentage of pie graph is Hockey and volleyball?

3) What percentage of pie not Football and Basketball

4) What percentage of pie graph is Hockey and Handball and Football?

5) What percentage of pie graph is Basketball?

6) What percentage of pie not Handball and Paintball?

Probability of Simple Events

✍ **Solve.**

1) A number is chosen at random from 28 to 35. Find the probability of selecting factors of 5.

2) A number is chosen at random from 1 to 60. Find the probability of selecting multiples of 15.

3) Find the probability of selecting 4queens from a deck of card.

4) A number is chosen at random from 8 to 19. Find the probability of selecting factors of 3.

5) What probability of selecting a ball less than 6 from 10 different bingo balls?

6) A number is chosen at random from 1 to 10. What is the probability of selecting a multiple of 2?

7) A card is chosen from a well-shuffled deck of 52 cards. What is the probability that the card will be a king OR a queen?

8) A number is chosen at random from 1 to 20. What is the probability of selecting multiples of 5.

Answers of Worksheets – Chapter 9

Mean and Median

1) Mean: 8, Median: 8

2) Mean: 8.33, Median: 6.5

3) Mean: 7.85, Median: 8

4) Mean: 5, Median: 3.5

5) Mean: 6.14, Median: 7

6) Mean: 7.57, Median: 9

7) Mean: 8.5, Median: 7.5

8) Mean: 8.14, Median: 6

9) Mean: 29.28, Median: 22

10) Mean: 8.87, Median: 8.5

11) Mean: 31, Median: 28

12) Mean: 48.5, Median: 46

13) Mean: 39.106, Median: 45

14) Mean: 4.8, Median: 4

Mode and Range

1) Mode: 8, Range: 11

2) Mode: 13, Range: 17

3) Mode: 7, Range: 6

4) Mode: 12, Range: 6

5) Mode: 2, Range: 8

6) Mode: 1, Range: 19

7) Mode: 7, Range: 30

8) Mode: 6, Range: 11

9) Mode: 4, Range: 8

10) Mode: 5,10, Range: 8

11) Mode: 12, Range: 16

12) Mode: 3, Range: 13

13) Mode: 22, Range: 32

14) Mode: 13, Range: 11

Times Series

Day	Distance (km)
1	343
2	430
3	268
4	507
5	390

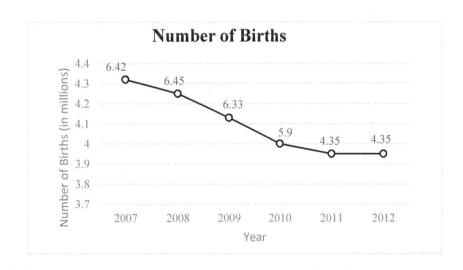

Number of Births

Box and Whisker Plots

1,3, 5, 8, 10, 11, 13, 14, 15, 17,18, 20, 23

Maximum: 23, Minimum: 2, Q_1: 8, Q_2: 13, Q_3: 17

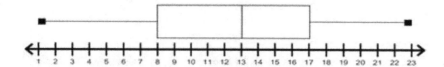

Bar Graph

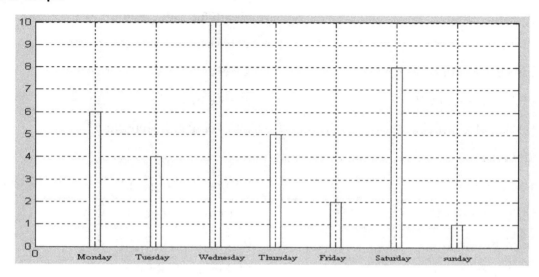

Dot plots

1) 4   3) 4   5) 1

2) 8   4) 6

Scatter Plots

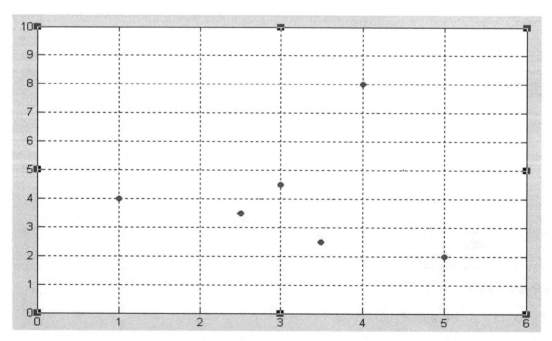

Stem–And–Leaf Plot

1)

Stem	leaf
1	2 4 7 8 9
2	1 3 4
4	2 4 7

2)

Stem	leaf
1	0 1 4 5 8
3	3 5 8
6	1 5 6 9

3)

Stem	leaf
8	6 7 8
9	1 2 9
10	0 7
12	1 2 6 9

4)

Stem	leaf
5	1 9 9
6	0 5 5 9
7	1 2 7
11	0 2 9

The Pie Graph or Circle Graph

1) 6%

2) 38%

3) 58%

4) 58%

5) 15%

6) 80%

Probability of simple events

1) $\frac{1}{4}$

2) $\frac{1}{15}$

3) $\frac{1}{13}$

4) $\frac{1}{3}$

5) $\frac{1}{2}$

6) $\frac{1}{2}$

7) $\frac{2}{13}$

8) $\frac{1}{5}$

9) $\frac{1}{13}$

ATI TEAS 6 Test Review

The ATI TEAS (Test of Essential Academic Skills), known as TEAS, is an admissions test for nursing schools, and is designed to assess a student's preparedness entering the health science fields. The last edition (the sixth edition) of the test, called the ATI TEAS 6 Test, was published by ATI Testing on August 31, 2016.

The ATI TEAS 6 Test consists of four multiple-choice sections:

- ✓ **Reading:** 53 Questions – 64 Minutes
- ✓ **Mathematics:** 36 Questions – 54 Minutes
- ✓ **Science:** 53 Questions – 63 Minutes
- ✓ **English and Language Usage:** 28 Questions – 28 Minutes

The Math portion will consist of around 36 multiple-choice questions that address The Math section of the test covers two main topics: Number and Algebra; Measurement and Data.

Students will be allowed to use a four-function calculator during the Math section of the ATI TEAS test. A calculator will be included in the online version and students will be issued one at the testing center during a paper and pencil test.

In this section, there are two complete ATI TEAS 6 Mathematics Tests. Take these tests to see what score you'll be able to receive on a real TEAS test.

Time to Test

Time to refine your skill with a practice examination

Take a REAL ATI TEAS 6 Mathematics test to simulate the test day experience. After you've finished, score your test using the answer key.

Before You Start

- ✓ You'll need a pencil, a timer, and a four-function calculator to take the test.
- ✓ After you've finished the test, review the answer key to see where you went wrong.
- ✓ Use the answer sheet provided to record your answers. (You can cut it out or photocopy it)
- ✓ You will receive 1 point for every correct answer. There is no penalty for wrong answers.

Good Luck!

ATI TEAS 6 Mathematics Practice Tests Answer Sheets

Remove (or photocopy) these answer sheets and use them to complete the practice tests.

ATI TEAS 6 Mathematic Practice Test

1	Ⓐ Ⓑ Ⓒ Ⓓ	13	Ⓐ Ⓑ Ⓒ Ⓓ	25	Ⓐ Ⓑ Ⓒ Ⓓ
2	Ⓐ Ⓑ Ⓒ Ⓓ	14	Ⓐ Ⓑ Ⓒ Ⓓ	26	Ⓐ Ⓑ Ⓒ Ⓓ
3	Ⓐ Ⓑ Ⓒ Ⓓ	15	Ⓐ Ⓑ Ⓒ Ⓓ	27	Ⓐ Ⓑ Ⓒ Ⓓ
4	Ⓐ Ⓑ Ⓒ Ⓓ	16	Ⓐ Ⓑ Ⓒ Ⓓ	28	Ⓐ Ⓑ Ⓒ Ⓓ
5	Ⓐ Ⓑ Ⓒ Ⓓ	17	Ⓐ Ⓑ Ⓒ Ⓓ	29	Ⓐ Ⓑ Ⓒ Ⓓ
6	Ⓐ Ⓑ Ⓒ Ⓓ	18	Ⓐ Ⓑ Ⓒ Ⓓ	30	Ⓐ Ⓑ Ⓒ Ⓓ
7	Ⓐ Ⓑ Ⓒ Ⓓ	19	Ⓐ Ⓑ Ⓒ Ⓓ	31	Ⓐ Ⓑ Ⓒ Ⓓ
8	Ⓐ Ⓑ Ⓒ Ⓓ	20	Ⓐ Ⓑ Ⓒ Ⓓ	32	Ⓐ Ⓑ Ⓒ Ⓓ
9	Ⓐ Ⓑ Ⓒ Ⓓ	21	Ⓐ Ⓑ Ⓒ Ⓓ	33	Ⓐ Ⓑ Ⓒ Ⓓ
10	Ⓐ Ⓑ Ⓒ Ⓓ	22	Ⓐ Ⓑ Ⓒ Ⓓ	34	Ⓐ Ⓑ Ⓒ Ⓓ
11	Ⓐ Ⓑ Ⓒ Ⓓ	23	Ⓐ Ⓑ Ⓒ Ⓓ	35	Ⓐ Ⓑ Ⓒ Ⓓ
12	Ⓐ Ⓑ Ⓒ Ⓓ	24	Ⓐ Ⓑ Ⓒ Ⓓ	36	Ⓐ Ⓑ Ⓒ Ⓓ

ATI TEAS 6 Practice Test 1

Mathematics

- **36 Questions**

- **Total time for this section:** 54 Minutes

- **Calculator is allowed at the test.**

Administered *Month Year*

1) The width of a garden is 5.42 yards. How many meters is the width of that garden?

    A. 4.96 m

    B. 404.1 m

    C. 54.2 m

    D. 194.1 m

2) The oven temperature reaches 50°C. What's the temperature in degree Fahrenheit?

$$C = \frac{5}{9}(F - 32)$$

    A. 50° F

    B. 122° F

    C. 82° F

    D. 46° F

3) How many meters is 26,123 centimeters?

    A. 26.123 m

    B. 2.612300 m

    C. 261.2300 m

    D. 2,612.300 m

4) If $x = 3$ what's the value of $2x^2 + 5x - 10$?

   A. 22

   B. 23

   C. 24

   D. 26

5) In six successive hours, a car travels 28 km, 19 km, 46 km, 33 Km, 53 km and 39 km. In the next six hours, it travels with an average speed of 38 km per hour. Find the total distance the car traveled in 12 hours.

   A. 415 km

   B. 407km

   C. 446 km

   D. 346 km

6) Find the mean of 113, 230, 240, 176, 250, and 253.

   A. 210.3

   B. 210.33 …

   C. 212.5

   D. 260

7) Solve the proportion. $\frac{1.2}{2.6} = \frac{x}{6.4}$

   A. 3.214

   B. 1.42

   C. 2.95

   D. 2.75

8) If $x + y = 14$, what is the value of $6x + 6y$?

    A. 124

    B. 64

    C. 108

    D. 84

9) The equation of a line is given as: $y = -3x + 2$. Which of the following points does not lie on the line?

    A. $(0, 2)$

    B. $(1, -1)$

    C. $(4, 9)$

    D. $(2, -4)$

10) If two angles in a triangle measure 40 degrees and 32 degrees, what is the value of the third angle?

    A. 108 Degrees

    B. 56 Degrees

    C. 96 Degrees

    D. 120 Degrees

11) If $4 + x \geq 15$, then $x \geq$?

    A. 6

    B. 12

    C. 11

    D. $15x$

12) What is the sum of $\frac{1}{16} + \frac{5}{2} + \frac{3}{8}$?

   A. 2.9

   B. 3

   C. $3\frac{2}{3}$

   D. 1

13) Last Friday Jacob had \$36.25. Over the weekend he received some money for cleaning the attic. He now has \$54. How much money did he receive?

   A. \$96.25

   B. \$17.75

   C. \$30.08

   D. \$15.58

14) Ella (E) is 6 years older than her friend Ava (A) who is 5 years younger than her sister Sofia (S). If E, A and S denote their ages, which one of the following represents the given information?

   A. $\begin{cases} E = A + 6 \\ S = A - 5 \end{cases}$

   B. $\begin{cases} E = A + 6 \\ A = S + 5 \end{cases}$

   C. $\begin{cases} A = E + 6 \\ S = A - 5 \end{cases}$

   D. $\begin{cases} E = A + 6 \\ A = S - 5 \end{cases}$

15) If x is 35% percent of 450, what is x?

    A. 56

    B. 157.5

    C. 160.5

    D. 150

16) If a rectangle is 40 feet by 53 feet, what is its area?

    A. 1,530

    B. 980

    C. 2,000

    D. 2,120

17) Six years ago, Ann was three times as old as Mia was. If Mia is 12 years old now, how old is Ann?

    A. 24

    B. 6

    C. 18

    D. 20

18) A number is chosen at random from 5 to 25. Find the probability of not selecting a composite number.

    A. $\frac{1}{5}$

    B. $\frac{1}{20}$

    C. $\frac{3}{10}$

    D. $\frac{7}{10}$

19) What is the value of x in this equation? $5(x + 7) = 75$

    A. 4

    B. 6

    C. 8

    D. 10

20) Simplify $\dfrac{\frac{1}{3} - \frac{x+2}{4}}{\frac{x^2}{3} - \frac{4}{3}}$

    A. $\dfrac{-3x+2}{3x^2 - 12}$

    B. $\dfrac{3x - 2}{6x^2 - 24}$

    C. $\dfrac{-3x - 2}{4x^2 - 4}$

    D. $\dfrac{-3x - 2}{4x^2 - 16}$

21) Two-kilograms apple and four-kilograms orange cost $36.8. If one-kilogram apple costs $2.4 how much does one-kilogram orange cost?

    A. $8

    B. $6

    C. $5.5

    D. $9

22) The average weight of 18 girls in a class is 57 kg and the average weight of 28

boys in the same class is 72 kg. What is the average weight of all the 46 students

in that class?

A. 66.32

B. 67.

C. 67.09

D. 66.13

23) A circle has a diameter of 2.4 inches. What is its approximate circumference?

A. 11

B. 8

C. 9

D. 12

24) In a certain bookshelf of a library, there are 45 biology books, 85 history books,

and 70 language books. What is the ratio of the number of biology books to the

total number of books in this bookshelf?

A. $\frac{1}{4}$

B. $\frac{9}{40}$

C. $\frac{7}{40}$

D. $\frac{3}{8}$

25) The circumference of a circle is 40cm. what is the approximate radius of the circle?

   A. 2.4 cm

   B. 6.4 cm

   C. 6.0 cm

   D. 7.5 cm

Questions 26 and 27 are based on following chart.

The following pie chart shows the expenses of Mr. Janson's family in December. The total expenses in December was $6,200.

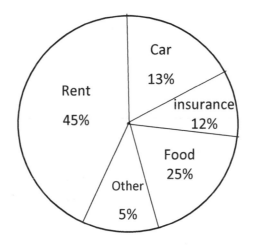

26) What percent of the expenses goes for car and rent combined?

   A. 58 %

   B. 48 %

   C. 36 %

   D. 66 %

27) How much did Mr. Janson's family spend on insurance?

A. $326

B. $744

C. $856

D. $1,040

28) A football team won exactly 60% of the games it played during last session. Which of the following could be the total number of games the team played last season?

A. 36

B. 33

C. 45

D. 16

29) I've got 32 quarts of milk and my family drinks 2 gallons of milk per week. How many weeks will that last us?

A. 2 Weeks

B. 2.5 Weeks

C. 3 Weeks

D. 4 Weeks

30) 5 liters of water are poured into an aquarium that's 20 cm long, 5 cm wide. How many cm will the water level in the aquarium rise due to this added water? (1 liter of water = 1,000 cm³)

A. 60

B. 50

C. 20

D. 8

31) At a Zoo, the ratio of lions to tigers is 6 to 2. Which of the following could NOT be the total number of lions and tigers in the zoo?

A. 32

B. 48

C. 95

D. 128

32) In a bundle of 80 pencils, 34 are red and the rest are blue. What percent of the bundle is composed of blue pencils?

A. 53%

B. 50%

C. 58%

D. 55%

33) If a inches of rain fall in two minutes, how many inches will fall in b hours?

 A. $30\frac{a}{b}$

 B. $30a$

 C. $30b$

 D. $30ab$

34) A card is drawn at random from a standard 52–card deck, what is the probability

 that the card is of King?

 A. $\frac{1}{3}$

 B. $\frac{1}{4}$

 C. $\frac{1}{6}$

 D. $\frac{1}{13}$

35) What is the value of the expression $3(5x + 6y) + (8 - 2x)^2$ when $x = 3$ and

 y= −2 ?

 A. 25

 B. 20

 C. 36

 D. 50

36) If a gas tank can hold 30 gallons, how many gallons does it contain when it is

$\frac{5}{6}$ full?

A. 60

B. 25

C. 62.5

D. 15

ATI TEAS 6 Practice Test 2

Mathematics

- **36 Questions**

- **Total time for this section:** 54 Minutes

- **Calculator is allowed at the test.**

Administered *Month Year*

1) In the simplest form, $\frac{18}{24}$ is

    A. $\frac{1}{3}$

    B. $\frac{3}{2}$

    C. $\frac{4}{3}$

    D. $\frac{3}{4}$

2) $\frac{(21\ feet + 5\ yards)}{4} = \underline{\quad}$

    A. 26 feet

    B. 20 feet

    C. 12 feet

    D. 9 feet

3) The sum of 7 numbers is greater than 560 and less than 630. Which of the following could be the average (arithmetic mean) of the numbers?

    A. 75

    B. 95

    C. 85

    D. 65

4) If $x = 7$, then $\frac{7^5}{x} =$

    A. 2,401

    B. 7,56

    C. 1,243

    D. 343

5) The distance between cities A and B is approximately 2,800 miles. If you drive

an average of 48 miles per hour, how many hours will it take you to drive from

city A to city B?

   A. approximately 52 hours

   B. approximately 58 hours

   C. approximately 48 hours

   D. approximately 35 hours

6) A swimming pool holds 2,450 cubic feet of water. The swimming pool is 35 feet

long and 10 feet wide. How deep is the swimming pool?

   A. 12

   B. 6

   C. 7

   D. 10

7) Chris is 15 miles ahead of Joe running at 5.5 miles per hour and Joe is running at

the speed of 8 miles per hour. How long does it take Joe to catch Chris?

   A. 8 hours

   B. 6 hours

   C. 3 hours

   D. 5 hours

8) A bread recipe calls for $4\frac{5}{9}$ cups of flour. If you only have $3\frac{2}{9}$ cups, how much more flour is needed?

   A. 1

   B. $\frac{4}{3}$

   C. 3

   D. $\frac{7}{9}$

9) The perimeter of a rectangular yard is 180 meters. What is its length if its width is twice its length?

   A. 30 meters

   B. 50 meters

   C. 60 meters

   D. 24 meters

10) If $7.4 < x \le 10.0$, then x cannot be equal to:

   A. 7.4

   B. 10

   C. 9.4

   D. 8.5

11) If $(4.2 + 3.2 + 6.6)\, x = x$, then what is the value of x?

   A. 1

   B. $\frac{1}{6}$

   C. 5

   D. 0

12) The equation of a line is given as: $y = 7x - 5$. Which of the following points does not lie on the line?

   A. $(1, 2)$

   B. $(-2, -19)$

   C. $(3, 18)$

   D. $(2, 9)$

13) If $a = 6$, what is the value of b in the following equation?

$$b = \frac{a^2}{4} + c$$

   A. $6 + c$

   B. $4 + c$

   C. $22 + c$

   D. $9 + c$

14) The sum of two numbers is x. If one of the numbers is 8, then two times the other number would be?

A. $2x$

B. $2 + x \times 6$

C. $2(x + 8)$

D. $2(x - 8)$

15) If $x = \dfrac{7}{3}$ then $\dfrac{1}{x} = ?$

A. $\dfrac{7}{3}$

B. $\dfrac{3}{7}$

C. 3

D. 7

16) Which of the following is the product of $1\dfrac{1}{4}$ and $5\dfrac{7}{6}$?

A. $7\dfrac{5}{24}$

B. $7\dfrac{17}{24}$

C. $7\dfrac{6}{9}$

D. $4\dfrac{2}{3}$

17) How many $\frac{1}{4}$ pound paperback books together weigh 50 pounds?

    A. 25

    B. 95

    C. 200

    D. 120

18) 6 feet, 20 inches +7 feet, 15 inches equals to how many inches?

    A. 191 inches

    B. 183 inches

    C. 194 inches

    D. 210 inches

19) $\frac{3}{5}$ is equals to:

    A. 0.6

    B. 0.8

    C. 0.03

    D. 0.28

Questions 20 and 21 are based on following Pie Chart.

The following pie chart shows the time Elise spent to work on his homework last week.

The total time Elise spent on his homework last week was 50 hours.

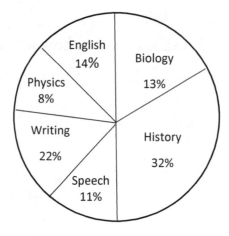

20) How much time did Elise spend on English last week?

    A. 3.5 hours

    B. 5 hours

    C. 6.5 hours

    D. 7 hours.

21) What many hours did Elise spend doing the Writing and Physics?

    A. 30 hours

    B. 22 hours

    C. 15 hours

    D. 8 hours

22) A circle has a diameter of 6 inches. What is its approximate circumference?

A. 6.28

B. 18.84

C. 34.85

D. 25.12

23) If a circle has a radius of 23 feet, what's the closest approximation of its circumference?

A. 144

B. 64

C. 164

D. 85

24) If two angles in a triangle measure 68 degrees and 35 degrees, what is the value of the third angle?

A. 8 degrees

B. 77 degrees

C. 86 degrees

D. 56 degrees

25) What is the sum of $\frac{1}{5} + \frac{3}{4} + \frac{5}{2}$?

A. 0.8

B. 3

C. $3\frac{1}{2}$

D. $1\frac{7}{20}$

26) Which of the following graphs represents the compound inequality?

$$-4 \leq 2x - 10 < 6$$

A.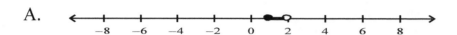

B.

C.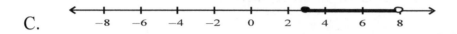

D.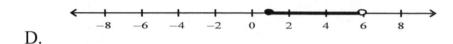

27) What is the equivalent temperature of 140°F in Celsius?

$$C = \frac{5}{9}(F - 32)$$

A. 58

B. 65

C. 60

D. 40

28) Julie gives 7 pieces of candy to each of her friends. If Julie gives all her candy away, which amount of candy could have been the amount she distributed?

A. 178

B. 216

C. 252

D. 223

29) With an 33% discount, Ella was able to save $30.24 on a dress. What was the original price of the dress?

A. $99.92

B. $91.64

C. $91.82

D. $99.92

30) The letters represent two decimals listed below. One of the decimals is equivalent to $\frac{1}{200}$ and the other is equivalent to $\frac{1}{25}$. What is the product of C and D?

0.ABC   0.0D

A. 0

B. 5

C. 25

D. 20

31) The marked price of a computer is D dollar. Its price decreased by 30% in January and later increased by 10 % in February. What is the final price of the computer in D dollar?

A. 0.70 D

B. 0.77 D

C. 0.80 D

D. 2.20 D

32) If two times a number added to 5 equals to 35, what is the number?

    A. 20

    B. 10

    C. 5

    D. 15

33) A bank is offering 3.0% simple interest on a savings account. If you deposit $21,000, how much interest will you earn in two years?

    A. $420

    B.$1,260

    C.$2,200

    D. $6,400

34) A football team had $25,000 to spend on supplies. The team spent $16,000 on new balls. New sport shoes cost $140 each. Which of the following inequalities represent how many new shoes the team can purchase?

    A. $140x + 16,000 \leq 25,000$

    B. $140x + 16,000 \geq 25,000$

    C. $16,000x + 140 \leq 25,000$

    D. $16,000x + 140 \geq 25,000$

35) What is the value of x in the following equation?

$$\frac{2}{5}x + \frac{1}{3} = \frac{1}{2}$$

A. 7

B. $\frac{1}{12}$

C. $\frac{5}{12}$

D. $\frac{1}{4}$

36) Two dice are thrown simultaneously, what is the probability of getting a sum of

5 or 7?

A. $\frac{2}{3}$

B. $\frac{2}{5}$

C. $\frac{5}{18}$

D. $\frac{2}{12}$

Answers and Explanations
ATI TEAS 6 Practice Tests

Answer Key

✻ Now, it's time to review your results to see where you went wrong and what areas you need to improve!

ATI TEAS 6 - Mathematics

Practice Test - 1				Practice Test - 2			
1	A	19	C	1	D	19	A
2	B	20	D	2	D	20	D
3	C	21	A	3	C	21	C
4	B	22	D	4	A	22	B
5	C	23	B	5	B	23	A
6	B	24	B	6	C	24	B
7	C	25	B	7	B	25	C
8	B	26	A	8	B	26	C
9	C	27	B	9	A	27	C
10	A	28	C	10	A	28	C
11	C	29	D	11	D	29	B
12	A	30	B	12	C	30	D
13	B	31	C	13	D	31	B
14	D	32	C	14	D	32	D
15	B	33	D	15	B	33	B
16	D	34	D	16	B	34	A
17	A	35	A	17	C	35	C
18	C	36	B	18	A	36	C

Answers and Explanations
ATI TEAS 6 - Mathematics
Practice Test 1

1) Answer: A

$$m = \frac{yd}{1.0936} \quad \rightarrow \quad m = \frac{5.42}{1.0936} = 4.9561082 \cong 4.96$$

2) Answer: B

Plug in 50 for C int the equation: $50 = \frac{5}{9}(F - 32)$

$450 = 5F - 160$

$450 + 160 = 5F \Rightarrow \frac{450 + 160}{5} = F$

$\frac{610}{5} = F \Rightarrow F = 122$

3) Answer: C

1 meter = 100 centimeters

$26{,}123 \times 0.01 = 261.23$

4) Answer: B

$2x^2 + 5x - 10 = 2(3)^2 + 5(3) - 10 = 18 + 15 - 10 = 23$

5) Answer: C

Add the first 6 numbers. $28 + 19 + 46 + 33 + 53 + 39 = 218$

To find the distance traveled in the next 6 hours, multiply the average by number of hours.

Distance = Average × Rate = $38 \times 6 = 228$

Add both numbers. $218 + 228 = 446$

6) Answer: B

Mean: $\frac{\text{sum of the data}}{\text{of data entires}} = \frac{113 + 230 + 240 + 176 + 250 + 253}{6} = \frac{1{,}262}{6} = 210.33$

7) Answer: C

$\frac{1.2}{2.6} = \frac{x}{6.4} \rightarrow x = \frac{1.2 \times 6.4}{2.6} = \frac{7.68}{2.6} = 2.95$

8) Answer: D

$x + y = 14$ Then: $6x + 6y = 14 \times 6 = 84$

9) Answer: C

Let's review the choices provided. Put the values of x and y in the equation.

A. $(0, 2)$ $\Rightarrow x = 0 \Rightarrow y = 2$ This is true!

B. $(1, -1)$ $\Rightarrow x = 1 \Rightarrow y = -1$ This is true!

C. $(4, 9)$ $\Rightarrow x = 4 \Rightarrow y = -10$ This is not true!

D. $(2, -4)$ $\Rightarrow x = 2 \Rightarrow y = -4$ This is true!

10) Answer: A

All angles in a triangle sum up to 180 degrees. Two angles add up to 90 degrees.

$40° + 32° = 72°$, then the third angle is: $180° - 72° = 108°$

11) Answer: C

$4 + x \geq 15$, $x \geq 15 - 4$, $x \geq 11$

12) Answer: A

$\frac{1}{16} + \frac{5}{2} + \frac{3}{8} = \frac{1+40+6}{16} = \frac{47}{16} = 2.937 = 2.9$

13) Answer: B

$54 - \$36.25 = 17.75$

14) Answer: D

Choice D represents the given information.

$E = 6 + A$, $A = S - 5$

15) Answer: B

$\frac{35}{100} \times 450 = 157.5$

16) Answer: D

Area of a rectangle = width × length = $40 \times 53 = 2,120$

17) Answer: A

Six years ago, Ann was three times as old as Mia. Mia is 12 years now. Therefore, 6 years ago Mia was 6 years. Six years ago, Ann was: $A = 3 \times 6 = 18$

Now Ann is 24 years old: $18 + 6 = 24$

18) Answer: C

The list of composite numbers from 5 to 25 is: 6, 8, 9, 10, 12, 14, 15, 16, 18, 20, 21, 22, 24, 25

There are 14 numbers in the list. Therefore, the probability of selecting a composite number is 14 out of 20 and the probability of not selecting a composite number is 6 out of 20 or $(\frac{3}{10})$.

19) Answer: C

Solve for x in the equation.

$5(x + 7) = 75 \to 5x + 35 = 75 \to 5x = 75 - 35 = 40 \to x = 40 \div 5 = 8$

20) Answer: D

Simplify:

$$\frac{\frac{1}{3} - \frac{x+2}{4}}{\frac{x^2}{3} - \frac{4}{3}} = \frac{\frac{1}{3} - \frac{x+2}{4}}{\frac{x^2-4}{3}} = \frac{\frac{4-3x-6}{12}}{\frac{x^2-4}{3}}$$

$$\Rightarrow \frac{-3x-2}{12} \div \frac{x^2-4}{3}$$

Then: $\frac{-3x-2}{12} \times \frac{3}{x^2-4} = \frac{3(-3x-2)}{12(x^2-4)} = \frac{-3x-2}{4(x^2-4)} = \frac{-3x-2}{4x^2-16}$

21) Answer: A

Let x be one-kilogram orange cost, then: $4x + (2 \times 2.4) = 36.8 \to 4x + 4.8 = 36.8 \to 4x = 36.8 - 4.8 \to 4x = 32 \to x = \frac{32}{4} = \$8$

22) Answer: D

$\text{average} = \frac{\text{sum of terms}}{\text{number of terms}}$

The sum of the weight of all girls is: $18 \times 57 = 1{,}026$ kg

The sum of the weight of all boys is: $28 \times 72 = 2{,}016$ kg

The sum of the weight of all students is: $1{,}026 + 2{,}016 = 3{,}042$ kg

Average $= \frac{3{,}042}{46} = 66.13$

23) Answer: B

Diameter $= 2r \Rightarrow 2.4 = 2r \Rightarrow r = 1.2$

Circumference $= 2\pi r \Rightarrow C = 2\pi (1.2) \Rightarrow C = 2.4\pi = 7.536 \cong 8$

24) Answer: B

Number of biology book: 45, total number of books; $45 + 85 + 70 = 200$

the ratio of the number of biology books to the total number of books is: $\frac{45}{200} = \frac{9}{40}$

25) Answer: B

$C = 2\pi r \Longrightarrow 40 = 2\pi r$

$r = \frac{40}{2\pi} = 6.36 \cong 6.4$

26) Answer: A

$45\% + 13\% = 58\%$

27) Answer: B

$\$6,200 \times \frac{12}{100} = \$744$

28) Answer: C

Choices A, C, and D are incorrect because 80% of each of the numbers is a non-whole number.

    A. 36   60% of $36 = 0.60 \times 36 = 21.6$

    B. 33   60% of $33 = 0.60 \times 33 = 19.8$

    C. 45   60% of $45 = 0.60 \times 45 = 27$

    D. 16   60% of $16 = 0.60 \times 16 = 9.6$

29) Answer: D

1 quart = 0.25 gallon

32 quarts = $32 \times 0.25 = 8$ gallons,

then: $\frac{8}{2} = 4$ weeks

30) Answer: B

One liter $= 1000$ cm$^3 \rightarrow$ *5 liters* $= 5,000$ cm^3

$5,000 = 20 \times 5 \times h \rightarrow h = \frac{5,000}{100} = 50$ cm

31) Answer: C

The ratio of lions to tigers is 6 to 2 at the zoo. Therefore, total number of lions and tigers must be divisible by 8.

$6 + 2 = 8$

From the numbers provided, only 95 is not divisible by 8.

32) Answer: C

$80 - 34 = 46$

$\frac{46}{80} = 0.58$

$0.58 \times 100\% = 58\%$

33) Answer: D

(hour: $\frac{2}{60} = \frac{1}{30}$); $\frac{a}{\frac{1}{30}} = \frac{x}{b} \rightarrow x = \frac{ab}{\frac{1}{30}} = 30ab$

34) Answer: D

The probability of choosing a king is $\frac{4}{52} = \frac{1}{13}$

35) Answer: A

$3(5x + 6y) + (8 - 2x)^2 = 3(5(3) + 6(-2)) + (8 - 2(3))^2 = 3(3) + (2)^2 = 9 + 4 = 13$

36) Answer: B

$\frac{5}{6} \times 30 = \frac{150}{6} = 25$

Answers and Explanations
ATI TEAS 6 - Mathematics
Practice Test 2

1) Answer: D

$$\frac{18}{24} = \frac{3}{4}$$

2) Answer: D

$1 \ yard = 3 \ feet$

$$\frac{(21 \ feet + 5 \ yards)}{4} = \frac{(21 \ feet + 15 \ feet)}{4} = \frac{(36 \ feet)}{4} = 9 \ feet$$

3) Answer: C

Let x be the average of numbers. Then:

$$\frac{560}{7} < x < \frac{630}{7}$$

$$80 < x < 90$$

From choices provided, only 85 is correct.

4) Answer: A

$$\frac{7^5}{7} = 7^4 = 2{,}401$$

5) Answer: B

$$\text{Speed} = \frac{distance}{time}$$

$$48 = \frac{2{,}800}{time} \rightarrow \text{time} = \frac{2{,}800}{48} = 58.33 \cong 58$$

6) Answer: C

$$\text{Volume} = \text{length} \times \text{width} \times \text{height}$$

$$2{,}450 = 35 \times 10 \times \text{height} \rightarrow \text{height} = 7$$

7) Answer: B

The distance between Chris and Joe is 15 miles. Chris running at 5.5 miles per hour and Joe is running at the speed of 8 miles per hour. Therefore, every hour the distance is 2.5 miles less.

$$15 \div 2.5 = 6$$

8) Answer: B

$$4\frac{5}{9} - 3\frac{2}{9} = 4 + \frac{5}{9} - 3 - \frac{2}{9} = 1\frac{3}{9} = 1\frac{1}{3} = \frac{4}{3}$$

9) Answer: A

Perimeter of a rectangle $= 2(width + length)$

$P = 180,\ width = 2 \times length$

Then: $180 = 2(2length + length) \rightarrow 180 = 6length \rightarrow length = 30$

10) Answer: A

If $7.4 < x \leq 10.0$, then x cannot be equal to 7.4.

11) Answer: D

$(4.2 + 3.2 + 6.6)\ x = x$

$14x = x$

Then $x = 0$

12) Answer: C

Let's review the choices provided. Put the values of x and y in the equation.

A. $(1, 2)$ $\Rightarrow x = 1 \Rightarrow y = 2$ This is true!

B. $(-2, -19) \Rightarrow x = -2 \Rightarrow y = -19$ This is true!

C. $(3, 18)$ $\Rightarrow x = 3 \Rightarrow y = 16$ This is not true!

D. $(2, 9)$ $\Rightarrow x = 2 \Rightarrow y = 9$ This is true!

Only choice C does not work in the equation.

13) Answer: D

If $a = 6$ then: $b = \frac{6^2}{4} + c \Rightarrow b = \frac{6^2}{4} + c = 9 + c$

14) Answer: D

Let a and b be the numbers. Then: $a + b = x$

$a = 8 \rightarrow 8 + b = x \rightarrow b = x - 8$

$2b = 2(x - 8)$

15) Answer: B

$$\frac{1}{x} = \frac{\frac{1}{7}}{\frac{7}{3}} = \frac{3}{7}$$

16) Answer: B

Converting mixed numbers to fractions, our initial equation becomes

$\frac{5}{4} \times \frac{37}{6}$,   Applying the fractions formula for multiplication

$\frac{5 \times 37}{4 \times 6} = \frac{185}{24} = 7\frac{17}{24}$

17) Answer: C

$50 \div \frac{1}{4} = 200$

18) Answer: A

1 foot = 12 inches

6 feet, 20 inches = 92 inches

7 feet, 15 inches = 99 inches

92 + 99 = 191

19) Answer: A

$\frac{3}{5} = 0.6$

20) Answer: D

Elise spent 14% of his total time (30 hours) on English. Then: $\frac{14}{100} \times 50 = 7$

21) Answer: C

Elise spent 30% of his time on Writing and Physics. Then: $\frac{30}{100} \times 50 = 15$

22) Answer: B

Circumference = $2\pi r$

C = $2\pi \times 3 = 6\pi$; $\pi = 3.14 \rightarrow$ C = $6\pi = 18.84$

23) Answer: A

Circumference = $2\pi r \rightarrow$ Circumference = 2(3.14)(23) = 144.44 $\cong$ 144

24) Answer: B

All angles in a triangle sum up to 180 degrees.

68 + 35 = 103

180 − 103 = 77,   The third angle is 77 degrees.

25) Answer: C

$\frac{1}{5}+\frac{3}{4}+\frac{5}{2}=\frac{4+15+50}{20}=\frac{69}{20}=3.45=3.5$

26) Answer: C

Solve for x.

$-4 \le 2x-10 < 6 \Rightarrow$ (add 10 all sides) $-4+10 \le 2x-10+10 < 6+10 \Rightarrow 6 \le 2x < 16 \Rightarrow$ (divide all sides by 2) $3 \le x < 8$

x is between 3 and 8. Choice C represent this inequality.

27) Answer: C

Plug in 140 for F in the equation:

$C = \frac{5}{9}(F-32) = \frac{5}{9}(140-32) = \frac{5}{9}(108) = 60$

28) Answer: C

Since Julie gives 7 pieces of candy to each of her friends, then, then number of pieces of candies must be divisible by 7.

A. $178 \div 7 = 25.43$
B. $216 \div 7 = 30.86$
C. $252 \div 7 = 36$
D. $223 \div 7 = 31.86$

Only choice C gives a whole number.

29) Answer: B

33% of $x = 30.24$

$x = \frac{100 \times 30.24}{33} \cong 91.64$

30) Answer: D

$\frac{1}{200} = 0.005 \to C = 5$, $\quad \frac{1}{25} = 0.04 \to D = 2 \to C \times D = 4 \times 5 = 20$

31) Answer: B

To find the discount, multiply the number by (100% – rate of discount).

Therefore, for the first discount we get: (D) (100% – 30%) = (D) (0.70) = 0.70 D

For increase of 10 %: (0.70 D) (100% + 10%) = (0.70 D) (1.10) = 0.77 D = 77% of D or 0.77D

32) Answer: D

Let x be the number. Then: $2x + 5 = 35$

Solve for x: $2x + 5 = 35 \rightarrow 2x = 35 - 5 = 30 \rightarrow x = 30 \div 2 = 15$

33) Answer: B

Use simple interest formula:

$I = prt$ (I = interest, p = principal, r = rate, t = time)

$I = (21,000)(0.030)(2) = 1,260$

34) Answer: A

Let x be the number of new shoes the team can purchase. Therefore, the team can purchase $140\ x$.

The team had $25,000 and spent $16,000. Now the team can spend on new shoes $9,000 at most.

Now, write the inequality:

$140x + 16,000 \leq 25,000$

35) Answer: C

$$\frac{2}{5}x + \frac{1}{3} = \frac{1}{2} \rightarrow \frac{2}{5}x = \frac{1}{2} - \frac{1}{3} \rightarrow \frac{2}{5}x = \frac{3-2}{6} \rightarrow \frac{2}{5}x = \frac{1}{6} \rightarrow x = \frac{5}{12}$$

36) Answer: C

To get a sum of 5 for two dice, we can get 4 different options:

(1, 4), (2, 3), (3, 2), (4, 1)

To get a sum of 7 for two dice, we can get 6 different options:

(4, 3), (3, 4), (2, 5), (5, 2), (1,6), (6,1)

Therefore, there are 10 options to get the sum of 5 or 7.

Since, we have $6\times 6 = 36$ total options, the probability of getting a sum of 5 or 7 is 10 out of 36 or $\frac{10}{36} = \frac{5}{18}$.

"End"

CPSIA information can be obtained
at www.ICGtesting.com
Printed in the USA
LVHW060906050720
659772LV00012B/667